Mills & Boon® Tender Romance™
is thrilled to present:

The First Man You Meet

by *New York Times* bestselling author

Debbie Macomber

A sparkling novella about meeting
'the one' – in the most unusual way!

When Shelly receives a wedding dress
as a gift, family legend says she will
marry the first man she meets – whether
he's the milkman, the postman – or
a gorgeous stranger!

Read on to discover who will
become her groom...

Debbie Macomber lives in Washington State, USA, with her husband. They have four grown-up children and are now proud grandparents. Debbie's successful writing career actually started in childhood, when her brother copied – and sold! – her diary. She's gone on to a considerably wider readership since!

Praise for Debbie Macomber:
"Ms Macomber…charms us with rich, dynamic characters, zestful scenes and tender dialogue."

Romantic Times

The First
Man You Meet

DEBBIE MACOMBER

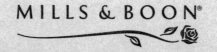

MILLS & BOON®

*MILLS & BOON and MILLS & BOON with the Rose Device
are registered trademarks of the publisher.*

*First published in Great Britain 1992
Harlequin Mills & Boon Limited,
Eton House, 18-24 Paradise Road, Richmond, Surrey, TW9 1SR*

The First Man You Meet © Debbie Macomber 1992

ISBN 0 263 82911 1

54-0103

*Printed and bound in Spain
by Litografia Rosés S.A., Barcelona*

Chapter One

IT HAD BEEN one of those days.

One of those hellish, nightmarish days in which nothing had gone right. Nothing. Shelly Hansen told herself she should have seen the writing on the wall that morning when she tripped over the laces of her high-top purple tennis shoes as she hurried from the parking lot to her dinky office. She'd torn a hole in the knee of her brand-new balloon pants and limped ingloriously into her building. The day had gone steadily downhill from there.

By the time she returned to her apartment that evening she was in a black mood. All she needed to make her day complete was to have her mother pop in unannounced with a man in tow, convinced she'd found the perfect mate for Shelly.

That was exactly the kind of thing Shelly had come to expect from her dear, sweet *desperate* mother. Shelly was twenty-eight now and single, and her mother tended to view her unmarried status as something to be remedied.

Never mind that Shelly felt content with her life just the way it was. Never mind that she wasn't interested in marriage and children...at least not yet. That time would come, she was sure, not now, but someday soon—or rather, some *year* soon.

For the moment, Shelly was absorbed in her career. She was proud of her work as a video producer, although she continually suffered the cash-flow problems of the self-employed. Her relaxation videos—seascapes, mountain scenes, a flickering fire in a brick fireplace, all with a background of classical music—were selling well. Her cat-baby-sitting video had recently caught the attention of a major distributor, and she couldn't help believing she was on the brink of being discovered.

That was the good news.

Her mother hounding her to marry was the bad.

Tossing her woven Mexican bag and striped blue jacket onto the sofa, Shelly ventured into the kitchen and sorted through the packages in her freezer until she found something to strike her fancy for dinner. The frozen entrée was in the microwave when the doorbell chimed.

Her mother. The way her day was going, it *had* to be her mother. Groaning inwardly, she decided she'd be polite but insistent. Friendly but determined, and if her mother began talking about husbands, Shelly would simply change the subject.

But it wasn't Faith Hansen who stood outside her door. It was Elvira Livingston, the building manager, a warm, delightful but insatiably curious older woman.

"Good evening, dear," Mrs. Livingston greeted her. She wore heavy gold earrings and a billowing, bright yellow dress, quite typical attire. She clutched a large box protectively in both hands. "The postman dropped this off. He asked if I'd give it to you."

"For me, Mrs. L.?" Perhaps this day wasn't a total waste, after all.

Elvira nodded, holding the package as though she wasn't entirely sure she should surrender it until she got every bit of relevant data. "The return address is California. Know anyone by the name of Millicent Bannister?"

"Aunt Milly?" Shelly hadn't heard from her mother's aunt in years.

"The package is insured," Mrs. Livingston noted, shifting the box just enough to examine the label again.

Shelly held out her hands to receive the package, but her landlady apparently didn't notice.

"I had to sign for it." This, too, seemed to be of great importance. "And there's a letter attached," Mrs. Livingston added.

Shelly had the impression that the only way she'd ever get her hands on the parcel was to let Mrs. Livingston open it first.

"I certainly appreciate all the trouble you've gone to," Shelly said, gripping the sides of the box and giving a firm tug. Mrs. Livingston released the package reluctantly. "Uh, thanks, Mrs. L. I'll talk to you soon."

The older woman's face fell with disappointment as Shelly began to close the door. Obviously, she was hoping for an invitation to stay. But after such a frustrating day, Shelly wasn't in the mood for company, especially not the meddlesome, if well-meaning, Elvira Livingston.

Shelly sighed. This was what she got for renting an apartment with "character." She could be living in a modern town house with a sauna, pool and workout room in an upper-class yuppie neighborhood. Instead she'd opted for a brick two story apartment building in the heart of Seattle. The radiators hissed at all hours of the night in perfect harmony with the plumbing that groaned and creaked. But Shelly loved the polished hardwood floors, the high ceilings with their delicate crystal light fixtures and the bay windows that overlooked Puget Sound. She could live without the sauna and the other amenities, even if it meant occasionally dealing with an eccentric busybody like Mrs. Livingston.

Eagerly she carried the package into the kitchen and set it on her table. Although she wondered what Aunt Milly had sent her, she carefully peeled the letter free, then just as carefully removed the plain brown wrapper.

The box was an old one, she noted, the cardboard heavier than that currently used by stores. Shelly gently pried off the lid and set it aside. She found thick layers of tissue paper wrapped around…a dress. Shelly pushed aside the paper and painstakingly lifted the garment from its box. She gasped in surprise as the long white dress gracefully unfolded.

This wasn't just any dress. It was a wedding dress, an exquisitely sewn lace-and-satin wedding dress.

Surely it couldn't have been Aunt Milly's wedding dress… No, that couldn't be… It wasn't possible.

Anxious now, her heart racing, Shelly carefully refolded the dress and placed it back in the box. She reached for the letter and discovered that her hands were trembling as she tore open the envelope.

My Dearest Shelly,

I trust this letter finds you happy and well. You've frequently been in my thoughts the past few days. I suppose you could blame Mr. Donahue for that. Though now that I think about it, it may have been Oprah. As you'll have gathered, I often watch those talk shows these days. John would have disapproved, but he's been gone eight years now. Of course, if I wanted to, I'd watch them if he were still alive. John could disapprove all he wanted, but it wouldn't do him a damn bit of good. Never did. He knew it and loved me, anyway.

I imagine you're wondering why I'm mailing you my wedding dress. (Yes, that is indeed my infamous wedding dress.) I suspect the sight of it has put the fear of God in you. I wish I could be there to see your face when you realized what I was sending you. No doubt you're familiar with its story; everyone in the family's known about it for years. Since you're fated to marry the first man you meet once the dress is in your hands, your first instinct is probably to burn the thing!

Now that I reconsider, I'm almost certain it was Donahue. He had a show recently featuring pets as companions to the elderly, lifting their spirits and the like. The man being interviewed brought along a cute little Scottish terrier pup and that was when the old seamstress drifted into my mind. I must have fallen asleep, because the next thing I knew the six o'clock news was on.

While I slept I had a dream about you. This was no ordinary dream, either. I saw you plain as day, standing beside a tall young man, your blue eyes bright and shining. You were so happy, so truly in love. But what amazed me was the wedding dress you were wearing.

Mine.

The very dress the old Scottish woman sewed for me all those years ago. It seemed to me I was receiving a message of some sort and that I'd best not ignore it. Neither had you! You're about to embark on the grandest adventure of your life, my dear. Keep me informed!

Believe me, Shelly, I know what you're thinking. I well remember my own thoughts the day that Scottish seamstress handed me the wedding dress. Marriage was the last thing on my mind! I had a career, back in the days when it was rare for a woman to attend college, let alone graduate from law school.

You and I are a great deal alike, Shelly. We value our independence. It takes a special kind of man to be married to women like us. And you, my dear niece, are about to meet that one special man just the way I did.

All my love,
Aunt Milly

P.S. You're only the second person to wear this dress, my dear. Never before have I felt like this. Perhaps it's the beginning of a tradition!

With hands that trembled even more fiercely now, Shelly folded the letter and slid it into the envelope. Her heart was pounding loud and fast, and she could feel the sweat beading her forehead.

The phone rang then, and more from instinct than any desire to talk, Shelly reached for the receiver.

"Hello." It hadn't dawned on her until precisely that moment that the caller might well be her mother, wanting to bring over a man for her to meet. Any man her mother introduced would only add to the growing nightmare, but—

"Shelly, it's Jill. Are you all right? You sound…a bit strange."

"Jill." Shelly was so relieved that her knees went weak. "Thank heaven it's you."

"What's wrong?"

Shelly hardly knew where to begin. "My aunt Milly's wedding dress just arrived. I realize that won't mean anything to you unless you've heard the family legend about my aunt Milly and uncle John."

"I haven't."

"Of course you haven't, otherwise you'd understand what I'm going through," Shelly snapped. She immediately felt guilty for being short-tempered with her best friend. Making an effort to compose herself, she explained, "I've just been mailed a wedding dress—one that's been in my family for nearly fifty years—with the clear understanding that I'll be wearing it myself soon."

"I didn't even realize you were dating anyone special." Jill hadn't managed to disguise the hurt in her voice.

"I'm *not* getting married. If anyone should know that, it's you."

"Then your aunt simply intends you to wear it when you do get married."

"There's far more to it than that," Shelly cried. "Listen. Aunt Milly—who's really my mother's aunt, a few years younger than my grandmother—became an attorney just after the Second World War. She worked hard to earn her law degree and had decided to dedicate her life to her career."

"In other words, she'd planned never to marry."

"Precisely."

"But apparently she did."

"Yes, and the story of how that happened has been in the family for years. It seems that Aunt Milly had all her clothes professionally made. As the story goes, she took some lovely white material to an old Scottish woman who had a reputation as the best seamstress around. Milly needed an evening dress for some formal event that was coming up—business related, of course. The woman took her measurements and told her the dress would be finished within the week."

"And?" Jill prompted when Shelly hesitated.

This was the part of the tale that distressed her the most. "And…when Milly returned for the dress the old woman sat her down with a cup of tea."

"The dress wasn't ready?"

"Oh, it was ready, all right, only it wasn't the dress Aunt Milly had ordered. The Scottish woman explained she was gifted with the 'sight.'"

"She was clairvoyant?"

"So she claimed," Shelly said, breathing in deeply. "The old woman told my aunt that when she began the dress a vision came to her. A clear vision that involved Milly. This vision apparently showed Milly getting married. The old woman was so convinced of it that she turned what was supposed to be a simple evening dress into an elegant wedding gown, with layers of satin and lace and lots of pearls."

"It sounds beautiful," Jill said with a sigh.

"Of course it's beautiful—but don't you see?"

"See what?"

It was all Shelly could do not to groan with frustration. "The woman insisted that my aunt Milly, who'd dedicated herself to her career, would marry within the year. It happened, too, just the way the seamstress said it would, right down to the last detail."

Jill sighed again. "That's the most romantic story I've heard in ages."

"It isn't romance," Shelly argued, "it's fate interrupting one's life! It's being a...pawn in the game of life! I know that sounds crazy, but I've grown up hearing this story. It was as though my aunt Milly didn't have any choice in the matter."

"And your aunt Milly mailed you the dress?"

"Yes," Shelly wailed. "*Now* do you understand why I'm upset?"

"Frankly, no. Come on, Shelly, it's just an old dress. You're overreacting. You make it sound as if you're destined to marry the next man you meet."

Shelly gasped audibly. She couldn't help herself. "How'd you know?" she whispered.

"Know what?"

"That's exactly what happened to Aunt Milly. That's part of the legend. She tried to refuse the dress, but the seamstress wouldn't take it back, nor would she accept payment. When Aunt Milly left the dress shop, she had car problems and needed a mechanic. My uncle John was that mechanic. And Aunt Milly married him. She married *the first man she met,* just like the seamstress said."

Chapter Two

"SHELLY, THAT doesn't mean *you're* going to marry the next man you meet," Jill stated calmly, far too calmly to suit Shelly.

Perhaps Jill didn't recognize a crisis when she heard about one. They were talking about destiny here. Predestination. Fate. Okay, maybe, just maybe, she was being a bit melodramatic, but after the ghastly day she'd had, who could blame her?

"Aunt Milly came right out and said I'm going to get married soon," Shelly explained. "The family legend says that the first man you meet when you get the dress is the man you'll marry."

"It's just coincidence," Jill reassured her. "Your aunt probably would have met her husband *without* the dress. It would've happened anyway. And don't forget, she's an old woman now," Jill continued soothingly. "I know this wonderful old lady who comes into the pharmacy every few weeks and she always insists *I'm* going to get married soon. I smile and nod and fill her prescription. She means well, and I'm sure your aunt Milly does, too. She just wants you to be happy, the way she was. But I think it's a mistake for you to take any of this prediction nonsense seriously."

Shelly exhaled sharply. Jill was right; Aunt Milly was a sweetheart, who had Shelly's happiness at heart. She'd had a long, blissful marriage herself and wanted the same for her great-niece. But Shelly had a career. She had plans and goals, none of which included meeting and marrying a stranger.

The story of Aunt Milly's wedding dress had been handed down from one generation to the next. Shelly had first heard it as a child and had loved it. In her young romantic heart, she'd ranked the story of her aunt Milly and uncle John with her favorite fairy tales of Cinderella and Sleeping Beauty, barely able to distinguish truth from fantasy. However, she was an adult now. Her heart and her life weren't going to be ruled by something as whimsical as a "magical" wedding dress or a fanciful legend.

"You're absolutely right," Shelly announced emphatically. "This whole thing is ridiculous. Just because this wedding dress supposedly conjured up a husband for my aunt Milly fifty years ago doesn't mean it's going to do the same thing for me, no matter what she claims."

"Well, thank goodness you're finally being sensible about this."

"No one bothered to ask me what I thought before shipping off a so-called magic wedding gown. I don't want to marry just yet, so I certainly don't need the dress. It was a nice gesture, but unnecessary."

"Exactly," Jill agreed.

"I'm not interested in playing déjà voodoo." She paused to laugh at her own joke.

Jill chuckled, too. "I wouldn't be, either."

Shelly felt greatly relieved and sighed expressively. The tight muscles along the back of her neck began to relax. Jill was, as usual, full of sound, practical advice. Aunt Milly was a wonderful old lady, and the legend was a delightful bit of family lore, but it would be laughable to take any of this seriously.

"How about meeting me for lunch tomorrow?" Jill suggested. "It's been ages since we got together."

"That sounds good to me," Shelly said eagerly. Although they'd been good friends since college, it took some effort on both their parts these days to make time in their hectic lives to see each other. "When and where?"

"How about the mall?" Jill asked. "That would be easiest for me since I'm scheduled to work tomorrow. I can get off a few minutes before twelve."

"Great. I'll see you at noon at Patrick's," Shelly promised. Meeting her friend for lunch was just the antidote she needed after the terrible day she'd suffered through. But then what did she expect on Friday, April thirteenth?

SHELLY OVERSLEPT, then got caught in a traffic jam on her way to meet Jill the following morning. She detested being late, although she often was. Rather than fight for a convenient parking spot in the vast lot that surrounded the mall, she took the first available space and rushed toward the nearest entrance. Patrick's, a cozy, charming restaurant on the mall's upper level, was deservedly popular for business lunches. Shelly had eaten there often and especially enjoyed the spinach-and-shrimp salad.

A glance at her watch told her it was already after twelve, and not wanting to keep Jill waiting, she hurried toward the escalator. The shopping center was especially busy on weekends, she noted, as she weaved her way around several people.

Her mind must have been on the salad she intended to order for lunch instead of the escalator because the moment she placed her foot on the first tread, she lost her balance.

"Oh...oh!" Swinging her arms out at both sides in a futile effort to remain upright, she groped at thin air. She tried frantically to catch herself as she fell backward.

Landing in someone's arms shocked her as much as having lost her balance. Incredulous, she twisted around to thank her rescuer but this proved to be a mistake. Her action caught the man off guard, and before he could prevent it, they both went crashing to the floor. Once again Shelly expected to experience pain. Instead, her waist was surrounded by arms that were surprisingly strong. His grip was firm but gentle, protective. As they fell, he maneuvered himself to take the brunt of the impact when they landed. Sprawled as she was above him, Shelly found herself staring down at the most attractive man she'd ever seen. Her heart thrummed. Her breath caught. Her body froze.

For a moment neither of them spoke. A crowd had gathered around them before Shelly managed to speak. When she did, her voice was weak and breathless. ''Are you all right? I'm so sorry…''

''I'm fine. What about you?''

''Fine. I think.''

She lay cushioned by his solid chest, their faces scant inches apart. Shelly's long hair fell forward, framing his face. He smelled of mint and some clean-scented soap. Her gaze wandered curiously over his features; at such close range she could see the tiny lines that fanned out from the edges of his sapphire-blue eyes as well as deep grooves that bracketed his mouth. His nose was classically straight, his mouth full and sensuous. At least his lower lip was. It didn't take her long to recognize that this man was uncompromisingly male. His eyes held hers reluctantly, as if he, too, was caught in the same powerful trance.

Neither of them moved, and although Shelly was convinced the breathless sensation she felt was a result of the fall, she couldn't seem to breathe properly even now.

''Miss, are you hurt?''

Reluctantly Shelly glanced up to find a security guard standing over her.

''Um…I don't think so.''

''Sir?''

"I'm fine."

The arms that were holding hers securely loosened.

"If we could have you both sit over here for a moment," the guard instructed, pointing at a bench. "We have an ambulance on the way."

"An ambulance? But I told you I'm not hurt," she objected.

The guard gently helped Shelly to her feet. Her legs were shaky and her breathing a bit uncertain, but otherwise she was unhurt.

"Officer, there's really no need—" the man who'd fallen with her protested.

"Mall policy," the guard interrupted. He hooked his thumbs into the wide leather belt and rocked gently back on his feet. "It's standard procedure to have all accident victims checked immediately."

"If you're worried about a lawsuit—"

"I don't make the rules," the guard interrupted her rescuer once again. "I just see that they're carried out. Now, if you'd both sit over here, the medical team will be here in a couple of minutes."

"I don't have time to wait," Shelly cried. "I'm meeting someone." She glanced longingly at the upper level, wondering how she could get word of her delay to Jill. It didn't reassure her to notice the number of people clustered by the railing, staring down at her. Her little escapade had attracted quite a bit of attention.

"I've got an appointment, as well," the man said, looking pointedly at his watch.

The security guard ignored their protests. He removed a small notebook from his shirt pocket and flipped it open. "Your names, please."

"Shelly Hansen."

"Mark Brady."

He wrote down the information and a brief account of how they happened to fall.

"I won't have to go to the hospital, will I?" Shelly demanded.

"That depends," the guard answered.

This whole thing was ridiculous. She was perfectly fine. A little shaken, true, but uninjured. She suddenly realized that she hadn't thanked this man—Mark, was it?

"I'm terribly sorry about all this," she offered. "I can't thank you enough for catching me."

"In the future, you might be more careful." Mark glanced at his watch a second time.

"I will be. But if it ever happens again, might I suggest you just let me fall?" This delay was inconvenient for her, too, but that wasn't any reason to be quick-tempered. She studied her rescuer and shook her head slightly, wondering why she'd been so impressed. He looked as if he'd stepped off the Planet Square. Dark blue suit and tie, crisp white shirt with gold cufflinks. This guy was as original as cooked oatmeal. About as personable, too.

If she was giving him the once-over, she discovered he was eyeing her, too. Apparently he was equally unimpressed. Her sweatshirt was a fluorescent orange and her jeans as tight as a second skin. Her ankle-high boots were black, her socks the same shade of orange as the sweatshirt. Her hair cascaded about her shoulders in a layer of dark frothy curls. Mark was frowning in obvious disapproval.

The wide glass doors at the mall entrance opened, and two paramedics hurried inside. Seconds later, when the ambulance arrived, two more medical people entered the building. Shelly was mortified that such a minor accident would result in all this attention.

The first paramedic knelt down in front of her while the second concentrated on Mark. Before she completely understood what was happening, her shoe was off and the man was examining her ankle. Mark, too, was being examined, a stethoscope pressed over his heart. He didn't seem to appreciate the procedures any more than she did.

It wasn't until he stood up that she realized how tall he was. Close to six-five, she guessed. A good match for her own five feet ten inches, she thought automatically.

It hit her then. Bull's-eye. Aunt Milly's letter had mentioned her standing beside a tall young man. Mark Brady was tall. Very tall. Taller than just about any man she'd ever met.

Aunt Milly's letter had also said something about Shelly's blue eyes. She'd ignored it at the time, but her eyes weren't blue. They were hazel. Mark had blue eyes, though. The kind of vivid blue eyes women generally found striking... Nor could she forget her initial reaction to him. She'd been attracted. Highly attracted. It'd been a long while since a man had interested her this much. Until he stood, anyway. When she got one good look at him, she'd known immediately that they had nothing in common. Mark Brady probably didn't own a single article of clothing that wasn't blue, black or tan. Clearly the man had no imagination.

On a sudden thought, she glanced worriedly toward his left hand. No wedding ring. Closing her eyes, she sagged against the back of the bench and groaned.

"Miss?" The paramedic was studying her closely.

"Excuse me," she said, straightening. She jerked impatiently on Mark's suit jacket. He was involved in a conversation with the ambulance attendant who was interviewing him and didn't turn around.

"Excuse me," she said again, louder this time.

"Yes?" Mark turned to face her, his gaze impatient.

Now that she had his attention, she wasn't sure she

should continue. ''This may sound like a silly question, but, uh…are you married?''

He frowned again. ''No.''

''Oh, no,'' Shelly moaned and slumped forward. ''I was afraid of that.''

''I beg your pardon.''

''Surely you've got a girlfriend—I mean, you're a tall, handsome kind of guy. There's got to be someone important in your life. Anyone? Please, just think. Surely there's someone?'' She knew she was beginning to sound desperate, but she couldn't help it. Aunt Milly's letter was echoing in her mind and all of last night's logic had disappeared.

The four paramedics, as well as Mark, were staring at her. ''Are you sure you don't want to come to the hospital and talk to a doctor?'' one of them asked gently.

Shelly nodded. ''I'm sure.'' Then before she could stop herself, she blurted out, ''What do you do for a living?''

''I'm a CPA,'' he answered wearily.

''An accountant,'' she muttered. She should have guessed. He was obviously as staid and dignified as he looked. And as boring. The type of man who'd probably never even heard of videos for entertaining bored house cats. He probably wouldn't be interested in purchasing one, either.

Surely her aunt Milly couldn't have seen Mark and Shelly together in her dream. Not Mark Brady. The two of them were completely ill-suited. A relationship between them wouldn't last five minutes! Abruptly she reminded herself that she wasn't supposed to be taking Aunt Milly's prediction seriously.

''May I go?'' she asked the paramedic. ''I'm not even bruised.''

''Yes, but you'll need to sign here.''

Shelly did so without bothering to read the statement.

Mark, however, seemed to scrutinize every sentence. He would, of course.

"Uh, Mark…" Shelly hesitated, and Mark glanced in her direction.

"Thank you," she said simply.

"You're welcome."

Still she delayed leaving.

"You wanted something else?"

She didn't know quite how to say this, but she felt the need too strongly to ignore it. "Don't take offense at this—I'm sure you're a really great guy…. I just want you to know I'm not interested in marriage right now."

Chapter Three

JILL WAS SEATED at the table, doodling on the paper place mat, when Shelly arrived. "What kept you?" she asked. "I've been here for almost half an hour."

"I—I fell off the escalator."

Jill's eyes widened in alarm. "My goodness, are you all right?"

Shelly nodded a bit sheepishly. "I'm fine…I think."

"Shouldn't you see a doctor?"

"I already have," she explained, avoiding eye contact with her friend. "Well, sort of. The security guard called in the paramedics. A whole bunch of them."

"No wonder you're late."

"I would have been, anyway," Shelly admitted as she reached for a menu, though she'd decided an hour earlier what she intended to order.

"This has really got you flustered, hasn't it?"

"It's more than the fall that's unsettled me," Shelly explained, lowering the menu. "It's the man who caught me."

Jill arched her eyebrows jokingly. "Aha! I should have guessed there was a man involved."

"You might try to understand how I felt," Shelly said reproachfully. "Especially since I haven't recovered from receiving Aunt Milly's wedding dress yet."

"Don't tell me you're still worried about that first-man-you-meet nonsense."

"Of course not. That would be ridiculous. It's just…it's

just I can't help feeling there might be something to that silly wedding dress.''

"Then mail it back."

"I can't," Shelly said, slapping the menu down on the table. "Aunt Milly warned me not to—though not exactly in those words, mind you. She said I shouldn't ignore the dress. I mean, how can I? It's like an albatross hanging around my neck."

"I still think you're overreacting to this whole thing."

"That's the crazy part. I *know* I am, but I can't seem to stop myself. I grew up hearing the legend of that wedding dress, and now it's in my possession. I've got a piece of family history hanging in the back of my closet. Heaven forbid if my mother should hear about this." She shuddered at that thought.

"So you hung the dress in your closet."

"I couldn't very well keep it under my bed. I tried that, but I couldn't sleep, so I finally got up and stuck it in the back of the closet." She closed the menu and set it aside. "That bothered me, too. I tossed and turned half the night, then I remembered Aunt Milly had done the same thing when the seamstress gave her the dress."

"She stuck it under her bed?"

Shelly nodded slowly. "I seem to remember hearing something like that. She'd tried to refuse it, but the old woman insisted Aunt Milly take the gown home with her. By the time she arrived at her apartment she'd already met my uncle John although she still didn't know she was going to marry him."

Jill raised a skeptical eyebrow. "Then what? After she put it under her bed and couldn't sleep, I mean?"

"Well, she did the same thing I did," Shelly admitted. "She shoved it into her closet." Shelly felt as if she were confessing to a crime. "I didn't want the thing staring me in the face so I hung it in the back."

"Naturally." Jill was trying, unsuccessfully, to disguise a smile. Shelly could see how someone else might find her situation humorous, but she personally didn't think any of this was too amusing. Not when it was her life, her future, being tossed around like some cosmic football. At this rate, she'd be married and with child by nightfall!

"That's not the worst of it," Shelly added. She exhaled slowly, wondering why her heart was still beating so fiercely.

"You mean there's more?"

She nodded. The waitress arrived just then and took their orders, returning quickly with tall glasses of iced tea. Shelly breathed in deeply before she continued. "I literally fell into that man's—Mark Brady's—arms."

"How convenient."

"It's all very nice of him to have broken my fall," she said sternly, "but I wish he hadn't."

"Shelly!"

"I mean it," she insisted. She glanced around, as if to make sure no one was listening, then added, "The man's an accountant."

Jill reacted in mock horror, covering her mouth with both hands and widening her eyes. "No! An accountant?"

"Think about it. Could you honestly picture me married to an accountant?"

Jill took a moment or two to mull over the question. "Hmm, a CPA," she repeated slowly. "You still haven't memorized your multiplication tables, have you? You freeze up whenever you have to deal with numbers. No, I guess you're right, I can't honestly see you with an accountant."

Shelly raised both hands, palms up, in a dramatic gesture. "I rest my case."

Jill reached for some bread, carefully selecting a whole-wheat roll. "Just because you fell into his arms doesn't mean you're going to marry him," she said in a matter-of-fact voice.

"I know that."

"Then what's the problem?"

"I can't make myself *believe* it," Shelly said. "I feel like one tiny pin fighting the force of a giant magnet."

"That's preposterous."

"I know," Shelly agreed readily. "I just wish I hadn't said anything to Mark."

Jill set the roll on her plate with exaggerated care. "You told him the story about your aunt Milly's wedding dress?"

"Of course not." Shelly was horrified her friend would suggest such a thing. "I just told him I couldn't marry him."

Jill's mouth dropped. "You didn't! Did you?"

Shelly nodded hesitantly. "I don't know what made me say anything so ludicrous. I honestly don't. I can't imagine what he must think of me. Not that I plan on seeing him again, of course. Unless—"

"Unless what?"

Their lunches were served. Jill had ordered a hot spinach salad with slices of chicken simmering in soy sauce sprinkled with sesame seeds. Shelly's spinach salad was piled high with shrimp, egg slices and black olives.

"Go on," Jill urged once the waitress had left the table. "You don't plan on seeing Mark again unless—"

"Unless it's unavoidable."

"I take it this means your aunt Milly's first encounter with your uncle John wasn't her last." Jill giggled. "Silly of me. Obviously it wasn't."

"No. Aunt Milly felt the same reluctance I do. My uncle was a wonderful man, don't get me wrong, and he was absolutely perfect for Aunt Milly, as it turned out, but the two of them were as different as night and day. Aunt Milly was a college graduate and Uncle John never completed high school.''

Shelly sighed wistfully. At one time the story of their romance had been like her own personal fairy tale. But now Shelly didn't find it nearly as enthralling. ''He helped Milly fix her car the night it broke down. The very next day she was in court defending a client in a law-suit—''

''Let me guess,'' Jill interrupted, ''your uncle John was the man suing her client.''

Shelly nodded. ''Yes, and that was only the beginning. Every time they turned around they were bumping into each other.''

''How long after they met were they married?''

This was the question Shelly had dreaded most. She closed her eyes and whispered, ''Ten days.''

''Ten days,'' Jill echoed with an incredulous look.

''I know. It seems that once they kissed they both realized there wasn't any use fighting it.''

''Did your aunt tell John about the seamstress and the wedding dress?''

Shelly shrugged. ''I don't know, but my guess is she didn't…at least not at first.'' She hadn't touched her salad yet and paused long enough to savor a forkful of her favorite seafood. Then she said abruptly, ''They eloped without telling anyone.''

''Children?'' Jill wanted to know.

''Three boys. My mother's cousins.''

''What about granddaughters? You'd think your aunt Milly would want to hand the dress down to one of them.''

''All three of her sons had boys themselves. I guess you could say I'm the closest thing she's got to a granddaughter.''

''Ten days,'' Jill repeated. ''That's really something.''

Forking up another succulent shrimp, Shelly continued her story. ''That old Scottish woman knew about the wedding even before the family did. When Aunt Milly and Uncle John returned from their honeymoon, there was a wedding card from the seamstress waiting for them at the house.''

Jill propped her elbows on the table and gazed at Shelly. ''Tell me what Mark Brady looks like.''

Shelly frowned, trying to form her impressions of him into some kind of reasonably articulate description. He was compelling in ways she didn't quite understand. Principled and headstrong, but how she knew that, Shelly couldn't explain. ''He's tall,'' she began slowly.

''How tall?''

''Basketball-player tall. He must be about six five.''

''Brown hair?''

Shelly nodded. ''With blue eyes. *Really* blue eyes. I can't remember the last time I met a man with eyes that precise color. They seemed to…'' She hesitated, unsettled by the emotion that stirred within her when she thought about Mark. Although their encounter had been brief, Shelly was left feeling oddly certain that she could trust this man, trust him implicitly. It wasn't a sensation she could ever remember experiencing with any other man. She didn't like the feeling; it made her uncomfortable. Until Jill had started asking her about Mark, Shelly didn't realize she'd experienced any emotion toward him—except for embarrassment, of course.

''Why do you want to know?'' she asked.

Jill gave her a silly, knowing grin. ''Because if he's as tall as you say, with dark brown hair and deep blue eyes, then the man you described just walked into this restaurant.''

''What?'' Shelly felt her stomach sink. ''Mark's here? Mark Brady?''

''That's not so amazing, is it? This is, after all, the same shopping mall in which you, uh, met—'' Jill made a show of glancing at her watch ''—thirty or so minutes ago.''

''He's here.'' She reminded herself that Jill was right: Mark's choosing to have lunch at Patrick's was just a logical coincidence. Too bad she couldn't convince her racing heart to believe that.

''He's sitting on the other side of the room,'' Jill whispered.

''Has he seen me yet?''

''I don't think so.''

Without being obvious—or at least Shelly hoped she wasn't being obvious—she turned to look in his direction. At that same instant, Mark happened to glance up. Their eyes met. Despite herself, she gasped. Her hands shook and she felt herself break out in a cold sweat.

Mark scowled and quickly looked away.

She couldn't blame him. He seemed surprised to see her there. Unpleasantly surprised.

''Well, is it him?'' Jill demanded.

Shelly couldn't find her voice, so she answered with a quick nod.

''I thought it might be. What are you thinking?''

''That I've lost my appetite.'' Shelly doubted she'd be able to finish her lunch.

''You want my advice?'' Jill asked, grinning broadly. ''I don't have a lot of experience in the area of magic wedding dresses, but I recently read a fascinating book on home remedies.''

''Sure.'' At this point Shelly was feeling reckless enough to try just about anything.

''Garlic,'' Jill said solemnly. ''Wear a garlic rope around your neck. Not only does it deter vampires, but it just might ward off potential husbands conjured up by a magic wedding dress.''

Chapter Four

HARD THOUGH SHE TRIED, Shelly had a difficult time ignoring Mark Brady. He sat there, stiff and unapproachable, at the other side of the small restaurant. Just as stiff and unapproachable as she was. Jill wanted to linger over her coffee before returning to her job at the PayRite Pharmacy in the mall, but Shelly was eager to be on her way. The sooner she left, the sooner she could put this bothersome encounter out of her mind.

"Don't forget Morgan's baby shower on Tuesday night," Jill said as Shelly reached for her purse.

Shelly had completely forgotten about their friend's party, which was understandable given her present state of mind. Most of their college friends were married and several were now having babies. Rather than admit how absentminded she'd suddenly become, Shelly asked, "Do you want to drive over together?"

"Sure," Jill agreed. "I have to go directly from work so I'll stop off at your place and we can leave from there."

"Sounds good to me." She tried to imagine their blond, scatterbrained classmate as a wife and mother. It was Morgan who'd gotten the entire dorm hooked on daytime soap operas. Before anyone could figure out how it had occurred, all the girls were obsessed with the characters and their lives. It became as important as mealtimes to learn if Jessie would ever find true love. To the best of Shelly's knowledge, she hadn't.

But then, Jessie didn't have an aunt Milly. The unexpected thought flashed through her mind.

Irritated with herself, Shelly dropped her share of the bill and a tip on the table. "I'll see you Tuesday, then."

"Right. And Shelly, don't look so worried. No enchanted wedding dress is going to disrupt your life unless you allow it to happen."

Easy for Jill to say, since it wasn't her life and her great-aunt's wedding dress. Nevertheless, her advice was sound. Aunt Milly might have had some fanciful dream about Shelly's marring a tall man with blue eyes, but that didn't mean it was going to happen, especially when Shelly was so determined that it wouldn't.

"You're absolutely right," she stated emphatically. "I know I keep saying that, but...well, I seem to need reminding. So, thanks. Again." With a final wave, she wandered out of the restaurant, barely noticing the colorful shop windows as she passed them. As Jill had pointed out, Aunt Milly meant well, but the letter and the wedding dress shouldn't be taken too seriously. Shelly was content with her life, and the last thing she needed right now was a man. Especially a staid, conventional man like Mark Brady.

Shelly knew exactly what kind of man she'd fall in love with. He'd be intelligent, and fervent about life, and as passionate as she was herself. Naturally, he'd appreciate her work and take pride in his own. He'd need to be a free spirit, like her. Unconventional. She'd like a man with gumption, too—someone who possessed a bit of initiative. It'd be nice if he was a little better at organizational skills than she was, but that wasn't absolutely necessary.

With thoughts of marriage so prominent in her mind, Shelly soon found herself standing in front of a jeweler's display window. A large assortment of wedding bands had captured her attention. Scanning the selection, she found one ring that stood out from the rest: three small rows of diamond chips, bracketed on each side by a thin band of gold. The ring was striking in its simplicity, its uncontrived beauty.

For the longest moment Shelly stared at the rings as her mind wove whimsical dreams around the happy bride and the tall groom. *Tall groom.* Her thoughts came to a skidding halt.

What on earth had come over her? She didn't know, but whatever it was, she didn't like it. Self-consciously she glanced around, fearful that someone was watching her. Well, a very specific someone, to be honest. Someone who definitely shouldn't see her gazing with open longing at a collection of absurdly high-priced wedding rings. Mark Brady.

With a sense of urgency, Shelly hurried toward the mall exit, her feet barely able to move fast enough. It was all she could do to keep from breaking into a run. No matter how fast she walked, however, she couldn't shake the feeling that *he* was there, watching her. Twice she whirled around, convinced she'd find Mark Brady strolling behind her, sneering and making contemptuous remarks.

He wasn't there.

Shelly felt herself relax as she neared her apartment. She parked her car, then stopped in the lobby to collect her mail. As soon as she opened the small box, Mrs. Livingston's head poked out her door.

"Good afternoon, Shelly," she chirped, gazing at her expectantly.

It took Shelly a moment to realize that Mrs. L. must have been waiting to hear about the contents of her package.

"It's a lovely day," Shelly said conversationally, sorting through her mail. Two bills, a flyer and something from the Internal Revenue Service. The way her luck had been going, it was probably an audit notice. A quick inspection revealed exactly that. She closed her eyes and groaned inwardly.

"A lovely day indeed," Mrs. Livingston echoed cheerfully.

Muttering under her breath, Shelly stuffed the IRS notice back inside the envelope. When she glanced up, she noticed that the older woman was now standing in the hallway, wearing another vividly colored outfit—turquoise and purple this time.

"I suppose you're wondering about the package," Shelly said resignedly, tucking her mail inside her purse. "It was a gift from my aunt Milly."

"Something from the past, I guess?" Mrs. Livingston asked.

"Why…yes, how'd you know?"

"I'd take whatever it was very, very seriously if I were you," Mrs. Livingston continued in a solemn voice. "Wizard wouldn't go anywhere near that box. Think what you want, but my cat has always had a sixth sense when it comes to this sort of thing."

"It's a dress, Mrs. L." Shelly explained, hiding behind a falsely bright smile. "How am I supposed to take a dress seriously?"

Mrs. Livingston opened her apartment door and scooped the large black-and-white cat into her arms. "That I wouldn't know," she returned, her eyes narrowed and mysterious. "All I can tell you is that Wizard felt skittish around that package. You don't suppose there's…magic in it, do you?"

Somehow Shelly managed a reply, although she felt certain it was unintelligible. Taking the stairs two at a time, she hurried into her apartment, leaning breathlessly against the door once she was inside. Even Mrs. Livingston's cat knew there was something strange about Aunt Milly's wedding dress!

WHEN JILL ARRIVED late Tuesday afternoon, Shelly was ready and waiting for her, brightly wrapped baby gift in hand. She was eager to get out and socialize—eager to get out, period. Anything to escape another phone call from her mother, who'd recently heard from Aunt Milly. Now Faith Hansen was calling daily for updates on the romantic prospects in her daughter's life.

"Well," Jill demanded as she entered the apartment. "Are you going to show it to me?"

"Show what to you?"

Jill gave her a look that seemed to question her friend's intelligence. "The wedding dress, of course."

For several hours Shelly had managed to put the dress out of her mind. "No," she said forcefully. "I want to forget about the whole thing."

"Met any tall blue-eyed men lately?" Jill couldn't resist asking.

"None," Shelly answered shortly. Checking her watch, she noted that they were early but suggested they leave, anyway. "Shouldn't we go now?"

"We've got lots of time," Jill countered, moving toward Shelly's bedroom. "Come on, it isn't going to hurt to let me look at the dress."

"Oh, all right," Shelly conceded ungraciously. Leading the way, she opened the closet door and reached into the back of the closet.

She brought out the lace-and-satin gown, holding it up for Jill's inspection. She'd barely looked at the dress the day she'd received it, and now she was almost shocked by how breathtakingly beautiful it actually was.

The laughter drained from Jill's dark brown eyes as she stared at the gown. "Oh, Shelly, it's…lovely." She gently touched the Elizabethan sleeve and ran her finger along the delicate layer of pearls that decorated the cuff. The high neckline was also trimmed with an intricate design of pearls, so that it resembled a choke collar. "I don't know what I expected," Jill continued in an awed whisper, "but certainly nothing as beautiful as this."

Shelly nodded wordlessly. The dress was far more exquisite than she'd realized. Her heart swelled with unexpected emotion, and to her dismay, tears filled her eyes as she thought about the old Scottish woman who had so lovingly constructed the gown. Each pearl had been sewn into place by hand. She thought of her aunt Milly, as tall and statuesque as Shelly herself, wearing the dress. Then she recalled her uncle John, such a determined man. She imagined him, standing tall and proud beside Milly. Shelly thought fondly of those two, who'd been so completely different, yet had loved each other so well....

For a moment neither she nor Jill spoke. "Have you tried it on?" Jill asked finally.

Shelly shook her head adamantly, not wanting her friend to realize how emotional she'd become. "Heavens, no, but you can if you want."

"I don't think I could resist if I were you," Jill whispered, obviously affected by the dress, too. "Just seeing it...makes me long to be a bride myself."

"There's always Ralph," Shelly teased. Jill had been dating Ralph, a computer programmer, for several months, but frankly she couldn't understand what her friend saw in him.

Jill tossed her an irritated look. "The dress is for you, not me."

"But I don't want it," Shelly insisted, though she was no longer sure what she felt. Not since she'd really examined the dress and allowed herself to remember the wonder of John and Milly's romance.

"You're sure you don't mind?" Jill asked, slipping off her shoes. "I mean, if you'd rather I didn't try it on, I'll understand."

"No, feel free." Shelly strove for a flippant air. "As far as I'm concerned the dress is nothing but bad luck. It arrived on Friday the thirteenth. The next day I had that minor accident on the mall escalator. Now I'm being audited by the IRS."

It was as if Jill didn't hear. "I doubt it'll fit," she said as she cautiously removed the gown from the padded hanger. "I'm a good five inches shorter than you and heavier on top."

"Maybe the dress was meant for you in the first place," Shelly ventured. Perhaps Aunt Milly had been confused and it was Jill she'd viewed in her dream. After all, Milly's eyes weren't what they used to be....

"Does your mother know?" Jill asked as she stepped into the dress. She raised it over her hips and turned around to let Shelly fasten the buttons that ran down the back.

"That's another thing," Shelly moaned. "Mom's been calling me every day since the dress arrived, wanting to know if I've met anyone special yet."

"What did you tell her?" Jill asked, looking at Shelly over her shoulder.

"What's there to tell?" she asked irritably.

"Well, you might have mentioned Mark."

"Mark," Shelly repeated. She shrugged elaborately. "I haven't given him a thought in days." Not strictly true, but she'd been *trying* not to think about him. Even if he was interested in her—and he'd made very clear that he wasn't—she couldn't imagine two more ill-suited people. "I haven't seen him since last Saturday and I doubt I'll ever see him again."

"You're sure of that?"

"Positive."

"Well, what do you think?" Jill asked next, pirouetting slowly in front of her. "My hair's a mess and I've got hardly any makeup on, but..."

Shelly looked at her friend and sighed audibly. Never had she seen Jill look lovelier. It was as if the dress had been made for her. "You look absolutely enchanting. It fits like a dream."

"I feel like I am dreaming," Jill admitted softly. "Here," she said, turning around, "undo me before I start longing for a husband and 2.5 children."

"Don't forget the house with the white picket fence," Shelly teased, unfastening the buttons.

Jill slipped out of the dress. "Your turn," she said as she laid it carefully across the bed. "If it fits me, then it can't possibly fit you. You've got the perfect excuse to mail it back to your aunt Milly."

"I...don't know." Shelly bit her lip. She felt an inexplicable urge to keep the dress, and at the same time she would've willingly express-mailed it back to her aunt. Even while she hesitated, Shelly found herself undressing. She couldn't explain her sudden eagerness to try on the wedding gown any more than she could fathom its growing emotional appeal.

The dress slid easily over her hips. She turned around so Jill could secure the back, then glanced toward the mirror, expecting to find the skirt miles too short. It would have to be in order to fit Jill as perfectly as it had.

"Shelly," Jill whispered, then cupped her hand over her mouth. "My goodness...you look beautiful...really beautiful."

The sentiment was what Shelly had felt when she'd viewed her friend in the dress. "Something's wrong," she said once she found her voice. "Something's very wrong."

"No," Jill countered, "it's very right. It's as if the dress was made for you."

"Then answer me this," Shelly whispered. "How is it possible for the same dress to fit two women who wear totally different sizes?"

Chapter Five

Shelly struggled to open the door of the Internal Revenue office, her arms weighted down with a huge box stuffed full of receipts and records she'd need for the audit. By bracing the box against the wall with her knee, she freed one hand to open the door. For the first time ever, she'd completed her tax return early—all by herself, too—and *this* was where it got her. She grumbled righteously and bit her lip, more in anxiety than annoyance.

She'd just managed to grasp the door handle, when the door unexpectedly opened and she staggered into the room, nearly colliding with an end table. She did a quick pirouette, convinced she'd ruined a new pair of panty hose. With a heartfelt sigh, she set her box of records on the floor and sank into the first available chair, neatly arranging her unaccustomed skirt around her knees. Only then did she bother to look around. There was one other person in the large reception area.

Shelly's heart did a nosedive, landing somewhere in the pit of her stomach. The man who'd opened the door for her, the man sitting in this very waiting room, was none other than Mark Brady—the man she'd hoped to avoid for the rest of her natural life. She gave an involuntary gasp.

Mark was leafing through the dog-eared pages of a magazine when he happened to glance her way. The automatic smile quickly faded from his face, and his gaze narrowed as if he strongly suspected Shelly had purposely arranged this meeting.

"What are you doing here?" Shelly demanded.

"I might ask you the same thing."

"I didn't follow you here, if that's what you're imply-
ing!"

"Listen, Ms....Hansen, I really couldn't care less."
With that he returned to his magazine as if he were reading
the fine print in a million-dollar contract. "*You're* the person who blurted out to everyone within hearing distance
that you weren't marrying me. As if I'd even asked! As if
I even *knew* you!"

Shelly felt the heat rising up her neck and quickly offered the first excuse she could think of. "I...was dis-
traught."

"Obviously," he muttered from behind his magazine.

A few minutes of strained silence passed. Shelly shifted
uncomfortably in her chair, checking her watch every couple of minutes. For the first time in recent history she was
early for an appointment, but if this was where promptness
got you, she'd prefer to be late.

"All right, I apologize," Shelly said when she couldn't
tolerate the silence any longer. "I realize it was utterly
ridiculous and...and out of turn—"

"Out of turn," Mark echoed, slapping the magazine
down on the table. "I repeat—I don't even know you."

"I realize that."

He inhaled deeply, which drew her attention to his
broad, muscular chest. She noticed that he was as metic-
ulously dressed as he'd been at their first encounter. His
dark suit and silk tie, however conventional, added a touch
of sophistication to his natural good looks.

"If there's anyone to blame for this it's Aunt Milly,"
Shelly said, more to herself than to him.

"Aunt Milly?" Mark repeated, sounding unsure. He
eyed her warily.

She'd said this much; she might as well launch into the
whole ridiculous tale.

"Actually, it has more to do with the wedding dress than with my aunt Milly, although by now the two of them are inseparable in my mind. I don't usually dabble in this sort of thing, but I'm beginning to believe there just might be something supernatural about that silly dress, after all."

"Supernatural?"

"Magic, if you prefer."

"Magic in a wedding dress?" Mark gazed hopefully at the door that led to the inner offices of Internal Revenue, as though he was anxious to be called away.

"It's unbelievable, but the dress fits both Jill and me—which is virtually impossible. You saw Jill—she's the friend I was having lunch with last Saturday. I know we were halfway across the room from you, but you couldn't help noticing how much shorter she is than I am. We're completely different sizes."

Mark hurriedly reached for the magazine as if he wanted to shut her out again before she said anything else.

"I know it sounds crazy. I don't like this any better than you do, but I'm honestly afraid it was you Aunt Milly mentioned in her letter." Well, it was only fair to tell him that.

Mark glanced in her direction again, blue eyes suspicious. "Your aunt Milly mentioned me in a letter?"

"Not by name—but she said she had a clear vision of me in the wedding dress and I was standing with a tall man. She also mentioned blue eyes. You're tall and you have blue eyes and the legend says I'm going to marry the first man I meet after receiving the dress."

"And I just happened to be that man?"

"Yes," Shelly cried. "Now do you understand why I was so disturbed when we met?"

"Not entirely," Mark said after a moment.

Shelly rolled her eyes. How obtuse could the man be? "You're tall, aren't you? And you have blue eyes."

He flipped intently through the magazine, not looking up at her as he spoke. "Actually, I really don't care what the letter said, nor am I concerned about this wedding dress you keep mentioning."

"Of course you don't care," Shelly said indignantly. "Why should you? It must all seem quite absurd to you. And I'm aware that I'm overreacting, but I do have a tendency to get emotional about things. If it helps any, I want you to know I'm content with my life just the way it is. I don't want to get married now—to anyone." When she'd finished, she sucked in a deep breath and began leafing idly through a magazine, doing her utmost to ignore him.

Silence returned. Silences had always bothered Shelly. It was as if she felt personally responsible for filling them. "If you want something to be grateful about, you can thank your lucky stars I didn't mention you to my mother."

"Your mother," Mark repeated, briefly glancing at her. "Does she know about Aunt Milly· sending you this… dress?"

"Naturally she does," Shelly answered, closing the magazine. "She's phoned me every day since she heard, because she thinks I'm going to meet that special someone any minute."

"And you didn't mention me?"

"How could I? The instant I do that, she'll be contacting the caterers."

"I see." The edges of his mouth lifted as though he was beginning to find the situation amusing. "She believes in the power of this dress, too?"

"Unfortunately, yes. You have to understand where my mother stands on this marriage business," Shelly continued, undaunted.

"I'm not sure I want to," Mark muttered under his breath.

Shelly disregarded his comment. "By age twenty-eight—my age now, coincidentally—Mom had been married for eight years and already had three children. She's convinced I'm letting the best years of my life slip away. There's nothing I can say to make her believe differently."

"Then I'll add my gratitude that you didn't mention me."

Mollified, Shelly nodded, then glanced at her watch. Her meeting was in ten minutes and she was nervous, since this was the first time she'd done her own taxes. She should have known there'd be a problem.

"I take it you're here for an audit?" Mark asked.

She nodded again, studying her tax return, sure she'd be in jail by nightfall without even understanding what she'd done wrong.

"Relax."

"How can I?"

"Have you knowingly hidden something from the government? Lied about the income you received, or claimed expenditures you've never made?"

"Oh, no!"

"Then you don't have anything to worry about."

"I don't?" Shelly stared at him, soaking up his confidence. She'd been restless for days, worrying about this meeting. If it wasn't the wedding dress giving her nightmares, it was the audit.

"Don't volunteer any information unless they ask for it."

"All right."

"Did you prepare your own tax return?"

"Well, yes. It didn't seem that complicated, and well, I realize this sounds silly but Jill bet me I couldn't do it. So I did. Back in February. You see, usually numbers boggle my mind and I decided to accept the challenge, and..." She realized she was chattering, something she did when she was nervous. Forcing herself to stay quiet, she scanned her return for the hundredth time, wondering what she could have possibly done wrong.

"Do you want me to check it over for you?"

Shelly was surprised by his generosity. "If you wouldn't mind. Are you being audited yourself?"

Mark smiled and shook his head. "A client of mine is."

"Oh."

Mark crossed the room and sat next to her. When Shelly handed him her tax return, his gaze ran quietly down the row of figures, then he asked her several questions.

"I've got everything right here," she assured him, gesturing toward the carton she'd lugged in with her. "I really am careful about saving everything I should."

Mark glanced down at the large cardboard box. "This is all for one year?"

"No," she admitted sheepishly. "I brought along everything I had for the past six years. I mean, it made sense at the time."

"That really wasn't necessary."

"I'd rather be safe than sorry," Shelly said, managing a small grin. She watched Mark as he scrutinized her return. At such close range, she saw that his eyes were even bluer than she'd thought. Blue as the sky on a bright July afternoon, she told herself fancifully. Her heart felt heavy in her chest, and hard as she tried, she couldn't keep from staring.

Mark handed back her return. "Everything looks fine. I don't think you'll have a problem."

It was amazing how relieved she felt at hearing that. No, at hearing that from *him*. Mark smiled at her and Shelly found herself responding readily with a smile of her own. The fluttery sensation returned to her stomach. She knew her eyes were wide and questioning and although she tried to look away, she couldn't make herself do it.

A look of surprise mingled with gentleness came over Mark's features, as if he were seeing her for the first time, really seeing her. He liked what he saw—Shelly could read that in his eyes. Slowly his gaze traveled over her features, and she felt her pulse tripping into double time. The letter she'd received from Aunt Milly flitted across her mind, but instead of dismissing the memory, she wondered, *Could there really be something to all this?*

Mark was the one to break eye contact. He stood abruptly and hurried back to his seat. "I don't think you have much to be concerned about."

"Yes, you told me."

"I mean about your aunt Milly's wedding dress."

"I don't have anything to worry about?" Shelly wasn't sure she understood.

"Not with me, at any rate."

"I don't quite follow..." If he was even half-aware of the way her heart was clamoring as they gazed into each other's eyes, he wouldn't be nearly as confident.

"I'm engaged."

"Engaged?" Shelly felt as though someone had slugged her in the stomach. Her first reaction was anger. "You couldn't have mentioned this sooner?" she snapped.

"It's not official yet. Janice hasn't picked out a diamond. Nor have we discussed our plans with her family."

The irritation faded, swallowed by an overwhelming sense of relief. "Engaged," she repeated, reminding herself that she really had no interest in marriage. And this proved there was no such thing as a "magic" wedding dress. If Mark was involved with Janice, he wouldn't be free to marry her. It was that simple. Shelly leaped to her feet and started to pace.

"Are you all right?" Mark asked. "You're looking pale."

She nodded and pressed her hands to her cheeks, which

suddenly felt hot. "I'm so relieved," she whispered hoarsely. "You have no idea how relieved I am. You're engaged... My goodness, I feel like I've got a new lease on life."

"As I explained," Mark said, frowning, "it isn't official yet."

"That doesn't matter. You're committed to someone else and that's all that matters. However—" she forced a smile "—you might have said something sooner and saved me all this anxiety."

"You did ask that day at the mall, but I was more concerned with avoiding a scene than revealing the personal details of my life."

"I'm sorry about that."

"No problem," Mark was quick to assure her.

Shelly settled back in the chair and crossed her legs, hoping to stroke a relaxed pose. She even managed to skim through a couple of magazines, although she barely knew what she was reading.

Finally, the receptionist opened the door and called her name. Eager to get this over with, Shelly stood, picking up the large box she'd brought in with her. She paused on her way out of the reception area and turned to Mark. "I wish you and Janice every happiness," she said formally.

"Thank you," he answered, then grinned. "The same to you and whomever the wedding dress finds for you to marry."

Chapter Six

SHE SHOULD BE HAPPY, Shelly told herself early the following morning. Not only had she survived the audit—in fact she'd come away with an unexpected refund—but she'd learned that Mark was practically engaged.

Yes, she should be dancing in the streets, singing in the aisles... Instead she'd been struggling with a strange melancholy ever since their last encounter. She seemed to have lost her usual vitality, her sense of fun.

And now it was Saturday, and for once she had no looming deadlines, no appointments, no pressing errands. Remembering the exhilaration and solace she'd experienced when she videotaped an ocean storm sequence recently, Shelly decided to see if she could recapture some of those feelings. She headed toward Long Beach, a resort town on the Washington coastline. The sky was clear and almost cloudless; the sun was bright and pleasantly warm—a perfect spring day. Once she drove onto the freeway, the miles sped past and two hours later she was standing on the sandy beach with the breeze riffling her long hair.

She walked around for a while, enjoying the sights and sounds about her, the chirping of the sea gulls, the salty spray of the Pacific Ocean and the scent of wind and sea. She was satisfied with the end product, her beach video, and started to work out plans for a whole series—the ocean in different seasons, different moods. That would be something special, she thought, something unique.

She wandered down the beach, kicking at the sand with the toe of her tennis shoes. Tucking her fingertips in the pockets of her jeans, she breathed in the vivid freshness around her. After an hour or so, she made her way back to the concession stands, where she bought a hot dog and a cold drink.

Then, just because it looked like such fun, she rented a moped.

She sped along the shore, thrilled with the sensation of freedom, reveling in the solitude and the roar of pounding surf.

The wind tossed her hair about her face until it was a confusion of curls. Shelly laughed aloud and listened as the galloping breeze carried off the sound.

Her motorized bike rushed forward, spitting sand in its wake. She felt reckless with exhilaration, as though there was nothing she couldn't do. It was that kind of afternoon. That kind of day.

When she least expected it, someone else on a moped raced past her. Shelly hadn't encountered anyone during her ride and this person took her by surprise. She glanced quickly over her shoulder, amazed by how far she'd traveled. The only other person she could see was the one who'd passed her.

To her surprise, the rider did an abrupt turnaround and headed back in her direction. With the sun in her eyes and the wind pelting against her, Shelly slowed to a crawl and she shaded her eyes with one hand.

It wasn't until he was nearly beside her that Shelly recognized the other rider.

Mark Brady.

She was so shocked that she allowed the engine to die, her feet dropping to the sand to maintain her balance. Mark appeared equally shocked. He braked abruptly.

"Shelly?" He seemed not to believe it was her.

Shelly shook her head and blinked a couple of times just to make sure she wasn't fantasizing. The last person

she'd expected to encounter on a beach two hours out of
Seattle was Mark Brady. Mr. Conservative on a moped!
This time, though, he wasn't wearing a dark suit. He didn't
have his briefcase with him, either. And he looked even
handsomer than usual in worn jeans and a University of
Washington sweatshirt.

"Mark?" She couldn't prevent the astonishment from
creeping into her voice.

"What are you doing here?" She heard the hostility in
his and answered him coolly.

"The same thing as you, apparently." She pushed the
hair from her face, and the wind promptly blew it back.

Mark's blue gaze narrowed suspiciously. "You didn't
happen to follow me, did you?"

"Follow you?" she repeated indignantly. She'd rarely
been more insulted. "Follow you!" she repeated, starting
her moped and revving the engine. "May I remind you
that I was on the beach first? If anyone was doing any
following, it was *you* following me." She was breathless
by the time she finished. "In light of our previous en-
counters, you're the last person I'd seek out."

Mark scowled at her. "The feeling's mutual. I'm not in
the mood for another story about your aunt Martha's damn
wedding dress, either."

Shelly felt an unexpected flash of pain. "I was having
a perfectly wonderful afternoon until you arrived," she
said stiffly.

"I was having a good time myself," Mark muttered.

"Then I suggest we go our separate ways and forget we
ever met."

Mark looked as if he were about to say something more,
but Shelly was in no frame of mind to listen. She twisted
the accelerator on the handlebar of her moped and took
off down the beach. Although she knew it was unreason-
able, she was furious. Furious at the surge of joy she'd felt

when she recognized him. Furious at Mark, because he didn't seem even a little pleased to see her. She bit her lower lip, remembering the comment he'd made about not wanting to hear anything more about her ''damn wedding dress.'' Now, that was just rude, she told herself righteously. She could *never* be interested in a man who was not only conventional but rude.

Squinting, Shelly hunched her shoulders against the wind, in a hurry now to return to the boardwalk area. She hadn't meant to go nearly this far.

The wet, compact sand made for smooth, fast riding and Shelly stayed close to the water's edge in an effort to out-distance Mark. Not that he was likely to chase her, but she wanted to avoid any possibility of another embarrassing encounter.

Then it happened.

A large wave came in, sneaking its way up the sand, creating a thin, glistening sheen. Shelly hardly noticed, as her front tire ripped through the water, spraying it out on both sides. Then the moped's front wheel dipped precari-ously. One minute she was sailing down the beach at breakneck speed and the next she was cartwheeling over her handlebars.

She landed heavily in a patch of wet sand, too paralyzed with shock to know if she was hurt or not.

Before she could move, Mark was crouching at her side. ''Shelly? Are you all right?''

''I…don't know.'' Carefully she flexed one arm and then the other. Sitting up, she tested each leg and didn't feel pain there, either. Apparently she'd survived the ex-perience unscathed.

''You crazy fool!'' he yelled, leaping to his feet. ''What are you trying to do, kill yourself?''

''Ah…'' It was painful to breathe just yet, otherwise she would have answered him.

"Can you imagine what I thought when I saw you flying through the air like that?"

"Good riddance?" she suggested.

Mark closed his eyes and shook his head. "I'm in no mood for your jokes. Here, let me help you up." He moved behind her, sliding his arms around her waist and gently raising her up.

"I'm fine," she protested the instant his arms surrounded her. The blood rushed to her head, but Shelly didn't know if that was because of her tumble or because Mark was holding her as though he never intended to let go. Even when she was on her feet, he didn't release her.

"Are you sure you're not hurt?"

Shelly nodded, not trusting her voice. "I'm less confident about the moped, though." Her bike seemed to be in worse shape than she was.

"It doesn't look good to me, either," Mark said. He finally dropped his arms and retrieved the moped, which was lying on its side, the waves lapping over it. There were regular hissing sounds as the cold water splashed against the heated muffler. Steam rose from the engine.

Mark did his best to start the bike for her, but to no avail. "I'm afraid it's hopelessly wet. It won't start now until it's had a chance to dry. A mechanic should check it over to be sure nothing's wrong."

Shelly brushed the hair from her face and nodded. There was no help for it; she was going to have to walk the bike back to the rental shop. No small feat when she considered she was about three miles down the beach.

"Thank you very much for stopping," she said a bit primly. "But as you can see I'm not hurt...."

"What do you think you're doing?" Mark asked as she began pushing the moped. It made for slow progress, the bulky machine was far more difficult to transport under her own power than she'd realized. At this rate, she'd be lucky to return it by nightfall.

"I'm taking the bike back to the place where I rented it."

"That's ridiculous."

"Do you have any better ideas?" she asked in a reasonable tone of voice. "I don't understand what you're doing here in the first place," she said, sounding far calmer than she felt. "You should be with Janet."

"Who?" he demanded. He tried to take the moped away from her and push it himself, but she wouldn't let go.

"The woman you're going to marry. Remember?"

"Her name is Janice and as I said before, the engagement's unofficial."

"That doesn't answer my question. You should be with her on a beautiful spring day like this."

Mark frowned again. "Janice couldn't get away. She had an important meeting with a client—she's a lawyer. Listen, quit being so stubborn, I'm stronger than you. Let me push the bike."

Shelly hesitated; his offer was tempting. She hadn't gone more than a few feet and already her side ached. She pressed one hand against her hip and straightened, her decision made. "Thanks, but no thanks," she answered flatly. "By the way, it's Aunt Milly who sent me the wedding dress, not Aunt Martha, so if we're going to get names straight, let's start there."

Mark rolled his eyes skyward, as though he'd reached the end of his limited reserve of patience. "Fine, I'll apologize for what I said back there. I didn't mean to insult you."

"I didn't follow you," she said.

"I know, but I didn't follow you, either."

Shelly nodded, finding that she believed him.

"Then how do you explain that we've inadvertently

stumbled into each other twice in the last week?'' Mark asked. ''The odds of that happening have got to be phenomenal.''

''I know it sounds crazy, but…I'm afraid it's the dress,'' Shelly mumbled.

''The wedding dress?'' Mark repeated.

''I'm really embarrassed about all this. I'm not sure I believe any of it myself. And I do apologize, especially since there's been an apparent mix-up—''

''Why's that?'' Mark asked.

''Well…because you're involved with Janice. I'm sure the two of you are a perfect match and you'll have a marvelous life together.''

''What makes you assume that?''

His question caught her off guard. ''Well, because… didn't you just tell me you're about to become officially engaged?''

''Yes,'' Mark muttered, frowning.

Although she was reluctant to admit it, Shelly found pushing the moped extremely taxing, so she stopped to rest for a moment. ''Listen,'' she said a little breathlessly, ''there's no need for you to walk with me. Why don't you just go on ahead?''

''There most definitely is a need,'' Mark answered sharply. He didn't seem too pleased with her suggestion. ''I'm not going to desert you now.''

''Oh, Mark, honestly, you don't have to be such a gentleman.''

''You don't like gentlemen?''

''Of course I do—but it's one of the reasons you and I would never get along for any length of time. You're very sweet, don't get me wrong, but I don't need anyone to rescue me.''

''Forgive me for saying so, but you *do* appear to need

rescuing.'' The look he gave her implied that he was referring to more than the moped.

"I was the one foolish enough to get the engine wet,''
she said brightly, ignoring his comment. "So I should be
the one to pay the consequences.''

Mark waited a moment, as if debating whether to continue arguing. "Fine, if that's the way you feel,'' he said
finally, straddling the moped and starting his engine, which
roared to life with sickening ease. "I hope you don't tire
out too quickly.''

"I'll be okay,'' she said, hardly able to believe he was
actually going to leave her.

"I hope you're right about that,'' he said, revving the
engine.

"You…you could let someone know,'' she ventured,
hoping the rental agency might send someone out with a
truck to find her.

"I'll see what I can do,'' he agreed, then grinning
broadly, took off at top speed down the beach.

Although she'd made the suggestion that he go on ahead
without her, Shelly had assumed he wouldn't take it seriously. She'd said it more for the sake of dignity, of pre-
serving her pride. She had actually been enjoying his company, enjoying the banter between them.

As he vanished into the distance, Shelly squared her
shoulders, determined to manage on her own—particularly
since she didn't have much choice in the matter. She'd
been dragging the moped along for several minutes when
she noticed a moped racing toward her. It didn't take her
long to identify the rider, with his lithe, muscular build, as
Mark. She picked up her pace, unreasonably pleased that
he'd decided to return. He slowed as he approached her.

"Still eager to be rid of me?''

"No,'' she admitted, smiling half in relief, half in pleasure. "Can't you tell when a woman means something and when she's just being polite?"

"I guess not." He smiled back, apparently in a jovial mood. "Rest," he said, parking his own moped and taking hers. "A truck will be along any minute."

Shelly sank gratefully into the lush sand. Mark lowered himself onto the beach beside her. She picked several blades of grass and began weaving them industriously together. That way, she wouldn't have to look at him.

"Are you always this stubborn?" he asked.

"Yes," she said quietly, giving him a shy smile. Shelly couldn't remember being shy in her life. But something about Mark made her feel shaky inside, and oddly weak. An unfamiliar sensation, but she dared not analyze it, dared not examine it too closely. She turned away from him and closed her eyes, trying to picture Janice, the woman he was going to marry. Despite her usually creative imagination, Shelly couldn't seem to visualize her.

"Shelly, what's wrong?"

"Wrong?"

"It's not like you to be quiet."

She grinned. They were barely more than acquaintances, and he already knew her. "Nothing."

"I think there must be." His finger against the side of her face guided her eyes toward him. Their lips were so close. Shelly's breath seemed to be caught somewhere in her throat as she stared helplessly into the bluest eyes she'd ever seen....

His forehead touched hers, then he angled his face gently, brushing her cheek. Shelly knew she should break away, but she couldn't make herself do it. Gently, deliberately, he pressed his mouth to hers, his lips warm and moist.

Shelly moaned at the shock of sensation. Her eyes drifted shut as his mouth moved hungrily over hers, and soon their arms were wrapped tightly around each other, their bodies straining closer.

The sound of the approaching truck intruded into their private world and broke them apart. Mark's eyes met hers, then he scowled darkly and glanced away. But Shelly didn't know whether he was more angry with her or with himself. Probably her.

Chapter Seven

"HEY," SHELLY SAID reassuringly, "don't look so concerned. It was just an ordinary, run-of-the-mill kiss." She stood indignantly and brushed the wet sand from her jeans. "Besides, it didn't mean anything."

Mark's scowl darkened. "Didn't mean anything?" he echoed.

"Of course it didn't! I mean, we were both wondering what it would be like, don't you think? Good grief, we seem to be running into each other every other day and it only makes sense that we should want to, you know, experiment."

"In other words, you think the kiss was just a means of satisfying our mutual curiosity?"

"Sure. All this nonsense about the wedding dress overcame our normal good sense, and we succumbed to the temptation." Thank goodness Mark seemed to understand her rambling. Shelly's knees were shaking. It was a wonder she could still stand upright. Although she'd tried to minimize the effects of his kiss, it left her feeling as though she'd never been kissed before. Her entire body had been overwhelmed by a feeling of rightness. Now all she felt was the crushing weight of confusion. She shouldn't be feeling any of these things for Mark. A CPA! An almost-engaged CPA, to boot.

"And was your curiosity satisfied?" he demanded. His blue eyes probed and waited.

"Uh...yes. And yours?"

"Yes," he muttered, but he was frowning again.

The youth from the rental agency leaped out of the truck and loaded Shelly's moped into the back. "You're not supposed to get the engine wet," he scolded. "It's in the rental agreement. You'll have to pay a fine."

Shelly nodded. She didn't have an excuse; she doubted the agency would accept her trying to escape Mark as a legitimate reason for damaging one of their vehicles.

Mark hefted his own bike onto the truck as well, and the three of them got into the pickup's cab and rode silently down the long stretch of beach.

Shelly went to the office to deal with her fine and was surprised to find Mark waiting for her when she'd finished. "You hungry?" he asked in an offhand invitation.

"Uh…" She would have thought he'd be anxious to see the last of her.

"Good," he said immediately, not giving her a chance to reply. His hand grasped her elbow firmly as he led her to a nearby fish-and-chips stand. Shelly couldn't recall the last time a man had taken her elbow. Her first reaction was to object to what she considered an outdated gesture but she was surprised to find it oddly comfortable, even pleasant.

They ordered their fish and chips, then carried the small baskets to a picnic table.

"I should have paid for my own," she said once they were seated, vaguely guilty that he'd paid for both meals. Janice might be the jealous type, and Shelly didn't want her to hear about this.

His eyes met hers, steady and direct. "When I ask you to join me, I pick up the bill."

Any argument she had vanished before it reached her lips.

After that, Shelly concentrated on her fish and chips, which were fresh and absolutely delicious. Mark seemed preoccupied with his meal, as well.

"What brought you to the beach today?" Shelly asked, finishing the last few French fries in her basket. Perhaps if they could figure out what had brought them both to a lonely stretch of beach two hours out of Seattle, they might be able to make sense of how they'd happened upon each other a third time.

"I have a beach house here. After tax time I generally try to get away for a few days, to come down here and relax."

"I had no idea." She found it inordinately important that he understand she hadn't somehow managed to stalk him across the state. Their meeting was pure coincidence…again.

"Don't worry about it, Shelly. You couldn't possibly have known about the beach house or that I intended to be here today. I didn't know it myself until this morning."

Shelly suddenly wished that Mark hadn't kissed her. Everything was becoming far too complicated now.

"You're very talented," he told her out of the blue. "I bought one of your videos the other day."

"How did you know what I do?" Shelly felt flustered by his praise; she was at a complete loss to understand why it meant so much to her.

"I saw it on the income tax form and I was curious about your work."

"Curiosity seems to have gotten us both into a great deal of trouble," she said.

Mark grinned, a shameless irresistible grin. The kind of grin that makes a woman forget all sorts of things. Like the fact that he was practically engaged. And that he was a tall, blue-eyed stranger who, according to Aunt Milly's letter, would soon become her husband.…

Shelly scrambled to her feet, hurrying toward the beach. Mark followed.

"You shouldn't look at me like that," she said, her voice soft and bewildered.

"You said it was just a kiss. Was it?"

"Yes," she boldly lied. "How could it be anything more?"

"You tell me."

Shelly had no answers to give him.

"While you're at it, explain why we keep bumping into each other or why I can't stop thinking about you."

"You can't?" She hadn't been able to stop thinking about him, either, but she wasn't ready to admit it.

"No." He stood behind her, his hands caressing her shoulders. Leisurely he stroked the length of her arms. His touch was so light that she thought she was imagining it, and she felt both excited and afraid.

He turned her around and gazed at her lips. "If that was just a run-of-the-mill kiss, then why do I feel the need to do it again?"

"I don't know."

His lips brushed hers. Briefly, with a whisper-soft touch, as though he was testing her response. Shelly closed her eyes and moaned. She didn't want to feel any of this. They were so far apart, such different people. Besides, *he* was involved with another woman and *she* was involved with her career.

When the kiss ended and he slowly released her, it was all Shelly could do to keep from sinking to the sand. "I have…to get back to Seattle," she managed to say, backing away from him. She turned and took four or five wobbly steps before she realized she was headed toward the Pacific Ocean.

"Shelly?"

"Yes?"

"Seattle is due north. If you continue going west, you'll eventually land in Hawaii."

"Oh, yeah, right," she mumbled, reversing her direction abruptly, eager now to escape.

THE FIRST PERSON Shelly called when she got home was Jill. "Can you come over?" Shelly asked without preamble. She could barely keep the panic out of her voice.

"Sure, what's wrong?"

"I saw Mark again."

"And?"

"Let me put it like this. We kissed and I haven't stopped trembling since."

Jill's romantic sigh came over the receiver as her breath softly caught. "This I've got to hear. I'll be there in ten minutes."

Actually it was closer to seven minutes. Shelly hadn't stopped pacing from the moment she got off the phone. She checked her watch repeatedly, waiting desperately for a dose of Jill's good sense.

"Shelly," Jill said, smiling as she breezed into the apartment, "what happened to your hair?"

Shelly smoothed down the errant curls. "I was at Long Beach."

"That's where you saw Mark? Good grief, that's something of a coincidence, isn't it?"

"I saw him earlier in the week, too.... Remember I told you I was being audited by the IRS? Lo and behold, guess who was in their waiting room when I arrived?"

"I don't need to be a rocket scientist to figure that one out. Mark Brady!"

"Right." Shelly rubbed her damp palms along her jeans in agitation. They, at least, had finally dried.

"And?"

Shelly groaned. "Can't you see what's happening? This is the third time we've been thrown together in the past few days. I'd never seen the man before, and all of a sudden he's around every corner. Then the wedding dress fit. It fit you…and it fits me.''

''I agree that's all rather odd, but I wouldn't put too much stock in it, if I were you.''

''Put too much stock in it… Listen, Jill, I've never had a man make me feel the way Mark does—all weak inside and, I don't know, special somehow. To be perfectly honest, I don't like it.'' She closed her eyes, hoping to chase away the memory of his touch, but it did no good. ''You want to know the real kicker?'' she asked abruptly, turning to face her friend. ''He's engaged.''

''Engaged,'' Jill echoed, her voice as startled as her expression.

''He keeps insisting it's not official yet. Nevertheless he's involved with someone else.''

''But it was you he kissed,'' Jill pointed out.

''Don't remind me.'' Shelly covered her eyes with both hands. ''I don't mind telling you, I find this whole thing unnerving.

''Obviously. Here,'' Jill said, directing Shelly toward the kitchen. ''Now sit down. Let me make us some tea, then we can try to reason this out. Honestly, Shell, I don't think I've ever seen you so upset.''

''I'm not upset,'' she cried. ''I'm confused. There's a big difference. I'm…I'm trapped.'' Despite all logic to the contrary, she couldn't help fearing that the entire course of her life was about to change because her aunt Milly had fallen asleep watching ''Donahue'' one day and had some nonsensical dream.

''Trapped?'' Jill repeated. ''Don't you think you're being a bit dramatic?''

''I don't know anymore.'' Shelly rested her elbows on the table, buried her face in her hands and breathed in deeply. She had a tendency to become emotional, especially over family issues; she realized that. But this was different. This was scary.

"Calm down," Jill advised. "Once you think it through in a rational manner, you'll realize there's a perfectly ordinary explanation for everything."

Jill's serenity lent Shelly some badly needed confidence. "All right, you explain it."

"I can't," Jill admitted matter-of-factly, pouring boiling water into Shelly's teapot. "I'm not even going to try. My advice to you is to quit taking all this so seriously. If a relationship develops between you and Mark, just enjoy it—providing the other woman's out of the picture, of course! Just forget about that dress."

"Easy for you to say."

"That's true," Jill agreed readily. "But you're going to have to accept it for your own peace of mind."

Shelly knew good advice when she heard it. "You're right. I'm unnecessarily leaping into the deep end with this."

"A dress can't make you do anything you don't want to do. The same applies to Mark."

Shelly always counted on her friend's levelheadedness. Although Jill had given her basically the same advice several days earlier, Shelly needed to hear it again.

Jill prepared two cups of tea and carried them to the table. "Are you going to be all right now?"

Shelly nodded. "Of course. I just needed a friend to remind me that I was overreacting." She took a sip of the tea, surprised by how much it revived her. "You're still planning to see *Street Suite* with me tomorrow afternoon, aren't you?"

The recent Broadway hit was showing locally, and Shelly and Jill had purchased their tickets several weeks earlier.

"That's not tomorrow, is it?" Jill looked stricken, her teacup poised midway to her mouth.

"Jill…"

"I promised I'd work for Sharon Belmont. She's got some family thing she has to attend. She was desperate and I completely forgot about the play. Oh, dear, you'll just have to go without me."

"You're sure you can't get out of it?" Shelly couldn't help feeling disappointed.

"I'm sure. I'm really sorry, Shell."

Although frustrated that Jill couldn't come with her, Shelly decided to go to the theater alone. She wasn't pleased at the prospect and given her proclivity for running into Mark Brady, she didn't feel entirely convinced that this wasn't another attempt by the fates to regulate their lives.

However, if she stayed home, she'd be missing a wonderful play. Not only that, she'd be giving in to a nebulous and irrational fear, allowing it to take over her life.

The following afternoon, Shelly dressed carefully, in the type of conservative outfit her mother would have approved of. Mark, too, would approve of her rose-colored linen dress with its matching jacket.… The minute the thought flashed through her head, she rejected it.

She was on her way out the door when her phone rang. For a split second she toyed with the idea of not answering. More than likely it was her mother, checking in to see if Shelly had met a prospective husband yet. Her calls had become more frequent and more urgent since Aunt Milly's dress had arrived.

Years of habit prompted her to reach for the telephone.

"Shelly." Mark's voice came over the line. "I was about to leave for the afternoon's performance of *Street*

Suite. Since we seem to have this tendency to run into each other everywhere we go, I thought I should probably clear it with you. If you're going to be there, I'll go another time.''

Chapter Eight

"ACTUALLY I WAS PLANNING to see the play this afternoon myself," Shelly admitted hesitantly. "Jill had to cancel out at the last minute."

"It seems Janice can't attend, either."

Hearing the other woman's name, the woman Mark loved, had a curious and unexpected effect on Shelly. Her heart sank, and she felt a sharp pang of disappointment. She rebounded quickly, however, forcing a lightness into her voice, a blitheness she didn't feel. "Listen, there's no need for you to miss the play. I'll call the ticket office and see about an exchange."

"No, I will," Mark offered.

"That's ridiculous. Jill really wanted to see this play and—"

"Would it really be so terrible if we both decided to attend the same performance?"

"Uh…" The question caught Shelly unprepared. Mark was the one who'd suggested they avoid each other.

"What could it possibly hurt? You have your ticket and I have mine. It'd be absurd to let them go to waste because we're afraid of seeing each other again, don't you think?"

Forming a single, coherent thought seemed beyond Shelly at that moment. After her long talk with Jill the day before, followed by the pep talk she'd given herself, she'd recovered a degree of composure. Now, all of a sudden, she wasn't sure of anything.

"I don't think it should matter," she said finally, although it did matter, greatly.

"Good. Enjoy the play."

"You, too."

The theater was within walking distance of her apartment building, and Shelly left as soon as she'd finished talking to Mark. He was right. Just because they each had tickets to the same play was no reason for either of them to be penalized.

So Mark was going to see *Street Suite*. It wasn't the type of play she would have thought he'd enjoy. But the man was full of surprises. Riding mopeds on the beach, kissing so spectacularly, and now this…

Shelly's mind was full of Mark as she hurried down the steep hill on Cherry Street. The theater was only a block away when she saw him. Her pulse soared and she wasn't sure if she should smile and wave or simply ignore him.

She didn't need to do either. He stood on the sidewalk, waiting for her.

"You're late," he said, glancing at his watch. "But then you traditionally are." His grin was wide and welcoming. "I couldn't see any reason not to watch the play together," he went on. "What do you say?"

"You're sure?"

"Positive." He offered her his arm, and she reflected that it was the kind of old-fashioned courtesy, the kind of gentlemanly gesture, she'd expected from Mark.

The usher seated them and smiled constantly as if to say they were a handsome couple. Shelly was terribly tempted to explain that Mark was engaged to someone else; luckily she managed to hold her tongue. Minutes after they'd settled into their seats, the curtain rose.

The play, a clever satire about urban life, was as good as the reviews claimed, and Shelly enjoyed herself thoroughly. Throughout the performance, however, she was all too aware of Mark sitting next to her. She found herself wondering if he was equally aware of her. She also found herself wondering how long it would be before they "bumped" into each other again—and hoped it was soon.

By the end of the play Shelly felt inspired and full of enthusiasm, eager to start a new project of her own. As she and Mark left the theater, she talked excitedly about her idea for the "ocean moods" series. He asked a few questions and even suggested some shots. Before she realized it, they were several blocks past the theater, headed in the opposite direction from her apartment building. Shelly paused and glanced around.

"There's an excellent Chinese restaurant in this neighborhood," was all Mark said. Without giving her the opportunity to decline, he gently guided her toward the place he'd mentioned.

It was early for dinner, and they were seated immediately. Although they'd been talking comfortably during their walk, Shelly found herself suddenly self-conscious. She toyed with the linen napkin, smoothing it across her lap.

"I hadn't expected to like the play as much as I did," he said after a while.

Shelly thought it a bit off that he'd ordered tickets for this production, but perhaps he'd gotten them because Janice had wanted to see *Street Suite*.

"It's a little frightening the way we keep finding each other, isn't it?" she ventured.

"I can see how *you'd* find it disconcerting," Mark answered.

"You don't?"

Mark shrugged. "I haven't given it much thought."

"I'll admit all these…coincidences do throw me," she said, running her index finger along the outline of the fire-breathing dragon on the menu cover. Chancing a glance in his direction, she added, "But I'm learning to deal with it."

"So you feel you've been caught in something beyond your control?" Mark surprised her by asking.

Shelly lifted her gaze to his, amazed by the intensity she read in his eyes. "No, not really. Well…a little bit, maybe. Do you?"

"It wasn't *my* aunt Milly who had the dream."

Shelly smiled and dropped her gaze. "No, but as my friend Jill reminded me recently, no fifty-year-old dress is going to dictate my life. Or yours," she felt obliged to add. Then she realized why he'd asked the question. "You must feel overwhelmed by all of this. All of a sudden I've been thrust into your life. There's no escaping me, is there?" she said wryly. "Every time you turn around, there I am."

"Are you going to stand up and announce to everyone in the restaurant that you refuse to marry me?"

"No." Shelly was appalled at his remark until she remembered that she'd done exactly that the first time they met.

"If you can resist doing that, then I think I can bear up under pressure."

Shelly ignored his mild sarcasm. "I'm not interested in marriage yet," she told him seriously—just in case he'd forgotten. "I'm content with my life. And I'm too busy for a husband and family."

She hadn't noticed how forcefully she was speaking until she saw several of the people at other tables glancing in her direction. Instantly she lowered her voice. "Sorry, my views on marriage seem to be more fervent than I realized. But I'm not about to let either my mother or my dear aunt Milly determine when I decide to settle down and marry."

"Personally, I can't see you ever settling down," Mark said with a small grin. "You don't have to worry. When you're ready, you'll know it."

"Did you?" She hadn't meant to bring up Janice, but now seemed as good a time as any to remind him—and her—that there was someone else in his life.

Mark shrugged casually. "More or less. I took a good, long look at my life and discovered I'd already achieved several of my professional goals. It was time to invest my energy in developing the personal aspects of my life. Marriage, children and the like."

Mark made marriage sound as if it were the next chapter in a book he was reading or a connect-the-dots picture. Shelly couldn't stop herself from frowning.

"You have a problem with that?"

"Not a problem, exactly. I happen to think of marriage a bit differently, that's all."

"In what way?"

He seemed genuinely interested, otherwise she would have kept her opinions to herself. "People should fall in love," she said slowly. "I don't think it's necessary or even possible to plan for that to happen. Love can be unexpected—it can take a couple by surprise, knock them both off their feet."

"You make falling in love sound like a bad case of the flu."

Shelly smiled. "In some ways, I think that's exactly how it should be. Marriage is one of the most important decisions in anyone's life, so it should be a *deeply felt* decision. It should feel inevitable. It's the union of two lives, after all. So you can't simply check your watch and announce 'it's time.'" She was suddenly concerned that she'd spoken out of turn and might have offended him, but one quick glance assured her that wasn't the case.

"You surprise me," Mark said, leaning forward. "I would never have guessed it."

"Guessed what?" She was beginning to feel a little foolish now.

"That a woman who gives the impression of being a scatterbrain is really quite reflective. Beneath those glow-in-the-dark sweatshirts lies a very romantic heart."

"I seem to have a tendency to get emotional about certain things," she answered, studying the menu, eager to change the subject. "I've heard hot-and-sour soup is wonderful. Have you ever tried it?"

Their conversation over dinner remained light and amusing. Shelly noticed that Mark avoided any more discussion of a personal nature, as did she.

After they'd finished their dinner and Mark had paid the bill, they leisurely strolled back toward the theater. Mark offered to drive her home when they reached his parked car, but Shelly declined. Her apartment was only a couple of blocks north and she preferred to walk.

Walk and think. Their time together had given her plenty to think about.

"Thank you for dinner," she said as he unlocked the car.

"You're welcome," he answered. "Well, good night for now," he said, grinning. "I suspect I'll be seeing you soon."

She grinned back. "Probably within a day or two. Maybe we should synchronize our schedules," she teased.

"That wouldn't bother you, would it?"

"Oh, no. What about you?" She hated the way her voice rose expectantly with the question. She certainly wasn't bothered by the prospect of seeing him again. In fact, she was downright eager to see what tricks fate would play on them next.

Mark's eyes found hers then, and he slowly pocketed his car keys. His look was so potent, so full of emotion, that Shelly took a step in retreat. "I had a wonderful afternoon, a wonderful evening. Thanks again," she said nervously.

Mark didn't say a word as he continued to gaze at her.

"The play was great, wasn't it? And dinner…fabulous." Shelly's throat seemed to close as Mark stepped onto the curb and walked toward her.

The whole world seemed to come to a sudden, abrupt halt when she realized he intended to kiss her. *Not again,* her mind shouted. *Please hurry,* her heart sang.

Her heartbeat tripped wildly as Mark lowered his head, his mouth seeking hers. Despite the fierce battle inside her, Shelly was forced to admit how much she wanted this kiss. If for no other reason, she told herself, than to prove that the first time had been an accident, a fluke.

Only it happened again. But this kiss was a hundred times more compelling than the first one they'd shared. A hundred times more exciting.

Shelly wanted to cry out at the unfairness of it all. If a man's kiss was going to affect her this acutely, why did it have to be Mark Brady's?

He broke away from her reluctantly, his warm breath fanning her cheek. His eyes were filled with questions, filled with surprise. Shelly wasn't sure what her own eyes were saying to him. She didn't even want to know.

"Take care," he whispered as he turned away.

SHELLY STAYED home from work on Monday. She wasn't sick, just confused and puzzled. Nothing about her relationship with Mark seemed to make sense. He was everything she *didn't* want in a man—and everything she did.

Shelly didn't realize how despondent she was until she found herself standing barefoot in front of her closet, carrying on a conversation with Aunt Milly's wedding dress.

"I'll have you know I had a perfectly good life until you arrived," she muttered disparagingly. "Now it seems my whole world's been turned upside down." She slammed the door closed, then jerked it open. "No wonder Mrs. Livingston's cat wouldn't go near you. You're *dangerous*."

Chapter Nine

"THE PLAY WAS GREAT," Shelly told Jill over coffee Wednesday afternoon. She'd stopped off at PayRite, hoping Jill could get away for lunch. "Even Mark—"

"Mark?" Jill's coffee cup hit the saucer with a clang. "He was at the play?"

Shelly nodded sheepishly. "I guess I forgot to mention I ran into him, didn't I? Actually he called me first and since we both had plans to attend the same performance, we decided to go together."

"Is there anything else you haven't told me?" Jill's eyes narrowed astutely.

Shelly tried to hide her uneasiness behind a relaxed shrug, but how well she succeeded in fooling Jill remained to be seen. "We had dinner afterward…as friends. It didn't mean anything. I did tell you he's engaged, didn't I?"

"*Unofficially* engaged." Jill was studying her closely and Shelly felt distinctly uneasy under the scrutiny.

"We've been friends for a long time," Jill reminded her. "In some ways I know you as well as I do myself. There's something troubling you."

Shelly nodded, knowing it wouldn't do any good to hide the truth from Jill. Her need to confide in a sympathetic, understanding person was the very reason for her impromptu visit to Jill's workplace. Lunch had been a convenient excuse.

"You won't believe this," Shelly said, cradling the warm coffee cup in both hands and keeping her gaze lowered. "I can hardly believe it myself."

"You're falling in love with Mark."

Shelly's gaze shot upward. "It shows that much?"

"No," Jill said softly. "But you look like you're about to break into tears."

"If I wasn't so darn irritated I would. Good grief, think about it. Can you imagine two people less suited to each other? Mark is so...so responsible..."

"So are you."

"Not in the same way," Shelly argued. "He's so sincere and..."

"Shelly, so are you."

"Perhaps, but I'm such a scatterbrain. I'm disorganized and always late and I like to do things my own way. You know that better than most."

"I prefer to think of you as creative."

Shelly tossed Jill a smile of appreciation. "That's the reason you're my best friend. I don't mind telling you, Jill, I'm worried. Mark Brady may be the Rock of Gibraltar, but I sincerely doubt he's got an original thought in his head. Everything is done by the book or according to schedule."

"You need someone like Mark in your life," Jill returned kindly. "Don't look so shocked. It's true. The two of you balance each other. He needs you because you're fun and crazy and imaginative, and you need him because he knows his times tables by heart and will remind you when it's time for meals."

"The problem is, Mark's the type of man who would expect a woman to *cook* those meals."

Jill chuckled.

"If the fates are determined to match me up with someone," Shelly moaned, "couldn't it be with someone other than an accountant?"

"Apparently not."

"What really angers me about this is that I allowed it to happen. The first time he kissed me—"

"He *kissed* you?" Jill feigned a look of horror.

Shelly ignored it. "Yes. A couple of times. It's only natural—our being curious about each other, don't you think?"

"I suppose," Jill said quickly, no longer teasing. "So tell me what happened."

"Fireworks bigger than the Fourth of July. I've never experienced the feelings I do with Mark, and all because of a simple kiss. I can't even begin to imagine what would happen if we ever made love."

"And does Mark feel the same thing?"

"I—I can't speak for him, but I think it must be equally disturbing for him. He certainly looked as if he'd been taken by surprise."

"How do you get along with him otherwise?"

"Fine, I guess." Shelly paused long enough to take a sip of her coffee. "I'm sure I amuse him. But someone like Mark isn't looking for a woman to entertain him, any more than I'm looking for a man to balance my checkbook."

"His opinion of you has mellowed, hasn't it?" Jill asked, then answered her own question. "There was a time when he thought you were a little bizarre, remember?"

Shelly did, all too well. "At first I thought he was about as exciting as oatmeal, but I've altered my opinion of him, too."

"So what's the problem?"

"I don't *want* to fall in love," Shelly said pointedly. "I've got bigger plans for my life than to tie myself down to a committed relationship right now."

"Then don't. It shouldn't be that difficult. Decide what you want and ignore everything else. There's no law that says you have to fall in love this minute. For that matter, no one can regulate when and who you marry, either. Not even your aunt Milly.''

Jill was saying everything Shelly wanted to hear. Everything she needed to hear. But it didn't make any difference; her heart was already involved. If she could forget she'd ever met Mark, she would. But it was too late. She was in love with him. With Mark, who was in love with someone else. Mark, who saw love and marriage as goals to be achieved within a certain time frame. He'd probably never done anything impulsive in his life.

A lasting relationship would never work between them. If he wasn't smart enough to figure that out, she was. Something had to be done and soon, and Shelly knew it would be up to her to do it.

SHELLY DIDN'T HAVE LONG to wait before she saw Mark again. They met at the main branch of the Seattle Public Library Wednesday evening. She was returning ten overdue books. Six months' overdue. The library had sent her three warnings, each one progressively less friendly.

She was half-afraid the buzzer just inside the library entrance would go off the moment she walked through the hallowed doors and armed officers would haul her away.

''I wondered how long it would take for us to find each other again,'' Mark said, strolling up to her at the counter. She'd seen him almost immediately and tried to pretend she hadn't.

Shelly acknowledged him with a quick nod and ordered her heart to be still. She managed a small smile. ''Hello again,'' she said, drawing the checkbook out of her purse. The fine for the books was sure to be monstrous. It might be cheaper to buy them.

Mark set the two volumes he was borrowing on the counter. Shelly noted the titles—*Tools for Time Management* and *The State of the Language,* and groaned inwardly. To someone like her accountant friend, these books were probably easy reading. Her own tastes leaned more toward mystery and romance, with a little nonfiction.

"Have you got time for a cup of coffee?" Mark asked as she wrote out the check to pay her fine.

Her heart was gladdened by the invitation, but she knew she had to refuse it. Before he could say or do anything to change her mind, she shook her head. "Not tonight, thanks."

His smile faded as though her refusal took him by surprise. "You're busy?"

She nodded, smiling at the librarian as she tore the check free and handed it to the woman, who smiled pleasantly in return. It had been a civilized exchange, Shelly thought, and her library card had *not* been confiscated, despite her transgressions.

"A date's waiting for you?"

It took Shelly a second to understand that Mark was referring to her refusal to join him for coffee.

"Not exactly." She turned away from the counter and headed toward the exit. To her surprise Mark followed her outside.

"Something's wrong," he said, standing at the top of the steps. She stopped her descent and stood below him, looking up. Pretense had never suited Shelly; she was too innately honest to hide her feelings. "Mark, I think you're a very nice man—"

"But you don't want to marry me," he concluded for her. "I've heard that line before, remember? Actually half the mall heard it, too."

"I've already apologized for that. It's just that…all right, if you must know, I'm beginning to like you…really like you, and frankly that terrifies me." She stood facing him, two steps below.

Her candid response seemed to unnerve him. He

frowned and rubbed the side of his jaw. "I know what you mean. I'm beginning to like you, too."

"See!" she cried, tossing her hands in the air. "If we don't take care of this problem now, heaven only knows what could happen. It has the potential of ruining both our lives. We're mature adults, aren't we?" At the moment, though, she felt singularly lacking in maturity.

All her senses were clamoring, telling her to enjoy their brief time together and damn the consequences. It was what her heart wanted, but she couldn't allow her life to be ruled by her heart. Not when it came to Mark.

"Liking each other doesn't have to be a federal crime," he said, advancing one step toward her.

"You're right, of course, but I know myself too well. I could easily fall in love with you, Mark." She didn't dare admit she already had. "Before we knew how it happened, we'd be spending more and more time with each other. We might even become seriously involved."

He remained suspiciously silent.

"You're a wonderful man. If my mother were to meet you she'd be shouting from the rooftops, she'd be so grateful. For a while I might convince myself that we could really make something of this relationship. I might even consider taking cooking classes because you're the kind of man who'd expect a woman to know how to make a roast and mashed potatoes."

"It'd probably come in handy someday," he admitted.

"That's what I thought," she murmured, disheartened. "I'm not a traditional woman. I never will be. The only time I ever baked a pie I ended up throwing it in the garbage disposal—and it broke the disposal."

"A pie ruined your garbage disposal?" Mark repeated, then shook his head. "Never mind, don't bother explaining how that happened. It seems to me you're getting ahead of yourself here. You're talking as though coffee together means a lifetime commitment.''

Shelly wasn't listening. ''What about Janice?'' she demanded. ''She's the one you should be inviting to coffee, not me.''

''What's Janice got to do with this?'' he asked impatiently.

''Janice,'' Shelly snapped, her own temper short. ''The woman you've decided to marry. Remember her? The love of your life? The woman you're unofficially engaged to marry.''

''It's not unofficial any longer,'' Mark explained evenly.

''Oh great, you're taking me out to dinner, kissing me and at the same time picking out engagement rings with another woman.'' She had to admit he'd never lied to her about his relationship with the faceless Janice. From the beginning he'd been forthright and honest about the other woman. But it hurt, really hurt, to learn that he was going ahead with his plans to marry Janice.

For a moment she'd been shocked into stillness. ''Then…'' She struggled to force some enthusiasm into her voice. ''Congratulations are in order. I wish you both the very best.'' With that she turned and bounded down the stairs, taking them recklessly fast.

''Shelly!''

She could hear Mark calling after her, but she ignored him, desperate to get away before the lump in her throat made it impossible to breathe. Tears had formed in her eyes and she cursed herself for being so ridiculous, for caring so much. Her vision blurred and she wiped a hand across her face, furious with herself for the lack of control. This marriage was what she'd hoped would happen. What she wanted for Mark. *Wasn't it?*

''Shelly, for heaven's sake, will you wait?''

When she reached the bottom of the steps, Shelly moved

quickly into a side street, hoping to disappear in the crowd, praying Mark wouldn't pursue her.

She thought she'd escaped until a hand on her shoulder whirled her around.

"Shelly, please listen," Mark pleaded breathlessly, his shoulders heaving with the effort of catching up with her. "The engagement isn't official, because there isn't an engagement. How could I possibly marry Janice after meeting you?"

Chapter Ten

"YOU BROKE OFF your engagement with Janice?" Shelly demanded furiously. Something inside, some reservoir of emotion, felt as if it had burst wide open. "You fool," she cried. "You idiot!" Her eyes brimmed over with tears and deep, deep inside her heart began its stirrings of glad excitement. "That was the worst thing you could have done!"

"No," he said. "It was the smartest move I've ever made."

"How can you say that?" she wailed.

"Shelly?"

He reached for her as though to offer comfort, but Shelly jerked her arms away and stepped back, freeing herself from his grasp. "Janice was perfect for you," she lamented.

"How do you know that?" he asked calmly, much too reasonably to suit Shelly. "You never met her."

"I didn't need to. I know she was right for you. You'd never have asked her to marry you if she wasn't."

"Janice is a wonderful woman and she'll make some lucky man a good wife, but it won't be me."

"You're crazy to break off your engagement. Crazy!"

"No, I'm not," Mark returned confidently. "I'm absolutely certain I did the right thing. Do you know why?"

Shelly could only shake her head, wiping away the tears with the back of her hand. She was ecstatic—and yet she was so frightened. She loved him, she was sure of it. Then why had everything become confused and difficult?

''What you said about love the other day changed my mind.''

''You listened to me?'' she cried in real horror. ''Do I look like an expert on love? I've never been in love in my life!'' Not counting what she felt for him, of course. She'd always thought love would clarify her life, not make it more complicated.

Mark ignored her outburst. ''You helped me understand that I was marrying Janice for all the wrong reasons. I'd decided it was time to settle down. Janice had come to the same conclusion. She's thirty and figured if she was going to marry and have a family, the time was now. It wasn't a love match, and we both knew it.''

''This is none of my business,'' Shelly said, frantically shaking her head as if to chase the words away. ''I don't want to hear any of it.''

''You are going to hear it,'' Mark insisted, gripping her elbows and gently drawing her closer to him. ''You claimed people shouldn't plan love. It should take them by surprise, you said, and you were right. Janice and I are fond of each other, but—''

''There's nothing wrong with fond!''

His eyes widened in obvious surprise. ''No, there isn't,'' he agreed, ''but Janice isn't a zany video producer. I like spending time with you. I've come to realize there's a certain thrill in expecting the unexpected. Every minute with you is an adventure.''

''A relationship between us would never last,'' Shelly insisted, drawing on the most sensible argument. ''It would be fine for a while, but then we'd drift apart. We'd have to. In case you haven't noticed, we're nothing alike.''

''Why wouldn't a relationship last?'' Mark asked patiently.

''For all the reasons I listed before!'' Mark was so endearing, and he was saying all the words she'd secretly longed to hear, but nothing could change the fundamental differences between them.

"So you aren't as adept in the kitchen as some women. I'm a fair cook."

"It's more than that."

"Of course it is," he concurred. "But there's nothing we can't overcome if we're willing to work together."

"You know what I think it is?" she said desperately, running her splayed fingers through her hair. "You're beginning to believe there's magic in Aunt Milly's wedding dress."

"Don't you?"

"No," she cried. "Not anymore. I did when I was a little girl…I loved the story of how Aunt Milly met Uncle John, but I'm not a child anymore, and what seemed so romantic then just seems unrealistic now."

"Shelly," Mark said in exasperation. "We don't need to do anything right away. All I'm suggesting is we give this thing between us a chance."

"There's nothing between us," she denied vehemently.

Mark's eyes narrowed. "You don't honestly believe that, do you?"

"Yes," she lied. "You're a nice guy, but—"

"If I hear any more of this nice-guy stuff I'm going to kiss you and we both know what will happen."

His gaze lowered to her mouth and she unconsciously moistened her lips with anticipation.

"I just might, anyway."

"No." The threat was real enough to cause her to retreat a couple of steps. If Mark kissed her, Shelly knew she'd be listening to her heart and not her head. And then *he'd* know… "That's what I thought." His grin was downright boyish.

"I think we should both forget we ever met," she suggested next, aware even as she said it how ludicrous she sounded. Mark Brady had indelibly marked her life and no matter how much she denied it, she'd never forget him.

"Are you forgetting you threw yourself into my arms? *You* can conveniently choose to overlook the obvious, but unfortunately that won't work for me. I'm falling in love with you, Shelly."

She opened her mouth to argue that he couldn't possibly love her...not yet, not on such short acquaintance, but he pressed his finger to her lips, silencing her.

"At first I wasn't keen on the idea," he admitted, "but it's sort of grown on me since. I can see us ten years in the future and you know what? It's a pleasant picture. We're going to be very happy together."

"I need to think," she cried, placing her hands on either side of her head. Everything was happening much too quickly; she actually felt dizzy. "We'll leave it to fate...how does that sound?" she offered excitedly. It seemed like the perfect solution to her. "The next time we bump into each other, I'll have more of a grasp on my feelings. I'll know what we should do." She might also take to hibernating inside her apartment for a month, but she wasn't mentioning that.

"Nope," Mark returned, slowly shaking his head. "That won't work."

"Why not?" she demanded. "We bump into each other practically every day."

"No, we don't."

He wasn't making any sense.

"*Street Suite* was a setup," he informed her. "I made sure we bumped into each other there."

"How? When?"

"The day at the beach I saw the play ticket sticking out of your purse. Our meeting at the theater wasn't any accident."

Mark couldn't have shocked her more if he'd announced

he was an alien from outer space. For the first time in recent memory, she was left speechless. "Tonight?" she asked when she could get the words out. "The library?"

"I'd decided to stop off at your apartment. I was prepared to make up some story about the wedding dress luring me into your building, but when I drove past, I saw you coming down the front steps loaded down with library books. It didn't take a whole lot of figuring to know where you were headed. I found a parking space and waited for you inside."

"What about…the IRS office and the beach?" She didn't know how he'd managed those chance meetings.

Mark shook his head and grinned. "Coincidence, unless you had anything to do with those. You didn't, did you?"

"Absolutely not," she replied indignantly.

Still grinning, he said, "I didn't really think you had."

Shelly started walking, her destination unclear. She felt too restless to continue standing there; unfortunately the one action that truly appealed to her was leaping into his arms.

Mark matched his own steps to hers.

"It's Aunt Milly's wedding dress, I know it is," Shelly mumbled under her breath. She'd tried to bring up the subject earlier, but Mark had refused to listen. "You broke off an engagement because you believe fate has somehow thrown us together."

"No, Shelly, the dress doesn't have anything to do with how I feel," Mark responded calmly.

"But you'd already decided to marry someone else!"

"I'm choosing my own destiny, which is to spend the rest of my life with you."

"You might have consulted with me first. I have no intention of getting married…not for years and years."

"I'll wait."

"You can't do that," she cried. He didn't understand

because he was too respectable and adorable and so much of a gentleman. The only thing that would work would be to heartlessly send him away before he wasted the better part of his life waiting for her.

She stopped and turned to face Mark. She was careful to wear just the right expression of remorse and regret. "This is all very flattering, but I don't love you. I'm sorry, Mark. You're the last person in the world I want to hurt."

For a moment Mark said nothing, then he slowly shrugged and looked away. "You can't be any more direct than that, can you? There's no chance you'll ever fall in love with me?"

"None." Her breath fell harshly, painfully, from her lips. It shouldn't hurt this much to do the right thing. It shouldn't hurt to be noble. "You're very nice, but..."

"So you've said before."

Falteringly, as though the movement caused him pain, he lifted his hand to her face, his fingers tenderly caressing the delicate curve of her jaw.

Until that moment, Shelly hadn't understood how fiercely proud Mark was. He could have dealt with every argument, calmed every doubt, answered every question, but there was nothing he could say when she denied all feeling for him.

"You mean it, don't you?" he asked huskily. He was standing so close that his breath warmed her face.

Shelly had schooled her features to reveal none of her clamoring emotions. His touch, so light, so potent, seemed to clog her throat with anguish, and she couldn't speak.

"If that's what you want—" he dropped his hand abruptly "—I won't trouble you again." With those words, he turned and walked away. Before she fully realized what he intended, Mark had disappeared around a corner.

"You let him go, you idiot!" she whispered to herself. A lone tear escaped and she smeared it across her cheek.

Mark meant what he said about not bothering her. He was a man of his word. He'd never try to see her again—and if they did happen upon each other, he'd pretend he didn't know her.

He might eventually decide to marry Janice. Hadn't he admitted he was fond of the other woman?

Shelly's heart clenched painfully inside her chest. Before she could stop herself, before she could question the wisdom of her actions, she ran after Mark.

She turned the corner and was halfway down the sidewalk when she realized he wasn't anywhere to be seen. She came to a skidding halt, then whirled around, wondering how he could possibly have gotten so far in so short a time.

Mark stepped out from the side of a building, hands on his hips, a cocky, jubilant smile on his face. "What took you so long, darlin'?" he asked, holding out his arms.

Shelly didn't need a second invitation to throw herself into his embrace. His mouth feasted on hers, his kiss hungry and demanding, filled with enough emotion to last a lifetime.

Shelly slid her arms around his neck and stood on her tiptoes, giving herself completely to his kiss, to his love. The only thing that mattered was being in his arms—where she was supposed to be.

"I take it this means you love me, too?" he whispered close to her ear. His voice was rough with emotion.

Shelly nodded. "I'm so afraid."

"Don't be. I'm confident enough for both of us."

"This is crazy," she said, but she wouldn't have moved out of his arms for the world. Breathing deeply, she buried her face in his chest.

"But it's a good kind of crazy."

"Aunt Milly saw us together in her dream. She wrote me about a tall, blue-eyed man."

"Who knows if it was me or not?" Mark whispered into her hair, and brushed his lips over her temple. "Who cares? If fate had anything to do with me finding you or if your aunt Milly's wedding dress is responsible, I can't say. Personally, I couldn't care less. I love you, Shelly, and I believe you love me, too."

She glanced up at this man who had altered the course of her life and smiled, her heart too full for words. "I do love you," she said when she could. "An accountant! In a suit! Hardly the husband I imagined for myself."

Mark chuckled. "I'd never have guessed I could find myself head over heels in love with a woman who wears the kind of clothes you do, but I am."

"I do love you," Shelly repeated and closed her eyes.

THE MORNING of her wedding day, Shelly, who was rarely nervous, couldn't sit still. Her mother was even worse, pacing in front of her, dabbing her eyes and sniffling.

"I can't believe my baby's getting married."

Shelly had to restrain herself from reminding her dear mother that less than a month before, she'd been desperate to marry her daughter off. Thank goodness Jill was around. Without her best friend there to reassure her, Shelly didn't know what she would have done. While her mother fussed with the caterers, complained to the florists and fretted about who had a key to the kitchen in the reception hall, Jill led Shelly upstairs to her childhood bedroom and helped her dress. When Shelly was finished, Jill stood back to examine her.

"Well?" Shelly asked, smoothing her hand down the antique dress, loving the feel of the satin and lace against her fingers. It was probably her imagination but now that she was wearing the dress, really wearing it, she could almost feel a magic quality.

Tears gathered in Jill's eyes as she stared at her friend.

"That bad?" Shelly teased.

Jill pressed her fingertips to her lips. "You're beautiful," she whispered. "Mark isn't going to believe his eyes when he sees you."

"Do you really think so?" Shelly hated sounding so insecure, but she wanted everything perfect for this day. She was crazy in love—and crazy enough to give her mother free rein planning her wedding. Crazy enough to go through with a formal wedding in the first place. If it had been up to her, they'd have eloped weeks ago. But Mark had wanted the wedding and her mother certainly wasn't going to be cheated out of this moment. So Shelly had gone along with it.

Mark and her mother had defeated the majority of her ideas. She'd wanted to hire clowns to entertain at the reception, but her mother didn't seem to think that was a good idea.

Shelly had never been that fond of white wedding cake, either. She wanted something a bit less traditional, like Cherries Jubilee, but Mark was afraid something might catch on fire and so in the interests of safety, Shelly had agreed to a traditional cake, decorated with pink roses.

A knock sounded on her bedroom door and Jill opened it. In walked Aunt Milly, looking absolutely delighted with herself.

She introduced herself to Jill, then turned to gaze lovingly at Shelly. "So I see the dress worked."

"It worked," Shelly agreed.

"You love him?"

Shelly nodded. "Enough to eat white wedding cake."

Milly laughed softly and sat on the edge of the bed. Her hair had faded to gray, but her eyes were still blue and clear. It was difficult to tell that she was a woman well into her seventies. She clasped both of Shelly's hands in her own.

"Nervous?"

Shelly nodded again.

"I was, too, although I knew to the very bottom of my heart that I'd made the right decision in marrying John."

"I feel the same way about Mark."

Aunt Milly hugged her tightly. "You're going to be very happy, my dear."

AN HOUR LATER Shelly and Mark stood at the front of a packed church with Pastor Johnson, who'd known her most of her life. He smiled warmly as he spoke a few words, then asked Shelly to repeat her vows.

Linking hands with Mark, she raised her eyes to his. Everyone else faded away. Aunt Milly. Jill. Her mother. There were only the two of them. She felt a jolt of pure joy at the love that radiated from Mark's eyes. He stood tall and proud, his gaze eagerly holding hers, the love shining through without doubt, without question, shining through for her to read. Shelly knew her eyes told him the same thing.

Later, Shelly couldn't remember speaking her vows aloud, although she was sure she did. The words came directly from her heart. Directly from Mark's.

They'd been drawn to this place and this time by forces neither fully understood. Shelly wasn't entirely sure she believed Aunt Milly's wedding dress was responsible, but it didn't matter. They were there out of love. She didn't know exactly when it had happened. Perhaps that day on the beach, when Mark first kissed her. Something had happened then, something that touched them both.

The love that began as a small spark had grown and

flared to life until they'd been brought here, to stand before God and family, pledging their lives to one another.

To love. To cherish. All the days of their lives.

It was enough. More than enough.

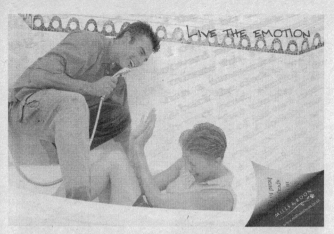

Historical Romance™
4 brand new titles each month
...rich, vivid
and passionate
Available on subscription every month
from the Reader Service™
GEN/04/RS2